MW00560781

THE ELEMENTS

Ingredients of the Universe

5th Edition

Written and illustrated by
Ellen Johnston McHenry

Also by this author:
"The Chemical Elements Coloring and Activity Book" ISBN 978-1-7374763-0-6

© 2021
(Original copyright 1999)
by Ellen Johnston McHenry
All rights reserved.

ISBN: 978-0-9887808-7-3

Ellen McHenry's Basement Workshop
www.ellenjmchenry.com
Pennsylvania, USA
ejm.basementworkshop@gmail.com

Also by this author:

The Chemical Elements Coloring and Activity Book
Carbon Chemistry
Dissect Your Dinner; Intro to Food Chemistry
Botany in 8 Lessons
Cells
The Brain
Rocks and Dirt
Protozoa: A Poseidon Adventure
Mapping the World with Art
Mapping the Body with Art
Introduction to Virology

Periodic Table of the Elements

Atomic Number →
Symbol
Name →
Atomic Weight

| 1 **H** Hydrogen 1.0 |

Legend example:

| 1 **H** Hydrogen 1.0 |

Group																	
1	2	3	4	5	6	7	8	9	10	11	12	13	14	15	16	17	18

1 **H** Hydrogen 1.0																	2 **He** Helium 4.0
3 **Li** Lithium 9.94	4 **Be** Beryllium 9.01											5 **B** Boron 10.8	6 **C** Carbon 12.01	7 **N** Nitrogen 14.0	8 **O** Oxygen 15.9	9 **F** Fluorine 18.9	10 **Ne** Neon 20.2
11 **Na** Sodium 22.9	12 **Mg** Magnesium 24.3											13 **Al** Aluminium 26.9	14 **Si** Silicon 28.0	15 **P** Phosphorus 30.9	16 **S** Sulfur 32.0	17 **Cl** Chlorine 35.4	18 **Ar** Argon 39.9
19 **K** Potassium 39.09	20 **Ca** Calcium 40.0	21 **Sc** Scandium 44.9	22 **Ti** Titanium 47.8	23 **V** Vanadium 50.9	24 **Cr** Chromium 51.9	25 **Mn** Manganese 54.9	26 **Fe** Iron 55.8	27 **Co** Cobalt 58.9	28 **Ni** Nickel 58.7	29 **Cu** Copper 63.5	30 **Zn** Zinc 65.4	31 **Ga** Gallium 69.7	32 **Ge** Germanium 72.6	33 **As** Arsenic 74.9	34 **Se** Selenium 78.9	35 **Br** Bromine 79.9	36 **Kr** Krypton 83.8
37 **Rb** Rubidium 85.4	38 **Sr** Strontium 87.6	39 **Y** Yttrium 88.9	40 **Zr** Zirconium 91.2	41 **Nb** Niobium 92.9	42 **Mo** Molybdenum 95.9	43 **Tc** Technetium (98)	44 **Ru** Ruthenium 101	45 **Rh** Rhodium 102.9	46 **Pd** Palladium 106.4	47 **Ag** Silver 107.8	48 **Cd** Cadmium 112.4	49 **In** Indium 114.8	50 **Sn** Tin 118.7	51 **Sb** Antimony 121.7	52 **Te** Tellurium 127.6	53 **I** Iodine 126.9	54 **Xe** Xenon 131.3
55 **Cs** Caesium 132.9	56 **Ba** Barium 137.3	57 **La** Lanthanum 138.9	72 **Hf** Hafnium 178.4	73 **Ta** Tantalum 180.9	74 **W** Tungsten 183.8	75 **Re** Rhenium 186.2	76 **Os** Osmium 190.2	77 **Ir** Iridium 192.2	78 **Pt** Platinum 195.0	79 **Au** Gold 196.9	80 **Hg** Mercury 200.6	81 **Tl** Thallium 186.2	82 **Pb** Lead 207.2	83 **Bi** Bismuth 208.9	84 **Po** Polonium (209)	85 **At** Astatine (210)	86 **Rn** Radon (222)
87 **Fr** Francium (223)	88 **Ra** Radium (226)	89 **Ac** Actinium (227)	104 **Rf** Rutherfordium (267)	105 **Db** Dubnium (268)	106 **Sg** Seaborgium (269)	107 **Bh** Bohrium (270)	108 **Hs** Hassium (269)	109 **Mt** Meitnerium (278)	110 **Ds** Darmstadtium (281)	111 **Rg** Roentgenium (282)	112 **Cn** Copernicium (285)	113 **Nh** Nihonium (286)	114 **Fl** Flerovium (289)	115 **Mc** Moscovium (289)	116 **Lv** Livermorium (293)	117 **Ts** Tennessine (294)	118 **Og** Oganesson (294)

| 58 **Ce** Cerium 140.1 | 59 **Pr** Praseodymium 140.9 | 60 **Nd** Neodymium 144.2 | 61 **Pm** Promethium (145) | 62 **Sm** Samarium 150.3 | 63 **Eu** Europium 151.9 | 64 **Gd** Gadolinium 157.25 | 65 **Tb** Terbium 158.9 | 66 **Dy** Dysprosium 162.5 | 67 **Ho** Holmium 164.9 | 68 **Er** Erbium 167.25 | 69 **Tm** Thulium 168.9 | 70 **Yb** Ytterbium 173 | 71 **Lu** Lutetium 174.9 |
| 90 **Th** Thorium (232) | 91 **Pa** Protactinium (231) | 92 **U** Uranium (238) | 93 **Np** Neptunium (237) | 94 **Pu** Plutonium (244) | 95 **Am** Americium (243) | 96 **Cm** Curium (247) | 97 **Bk** Berkelium (247) | 98 **Cf** Californium (251) | 99 **Es** Einsteinium (252) | 100 **Fm** Fermium (257) | 101 **Md** Mendelevium (258) | 102 **No** Nobelium (259) | 103 **Lr** Lawrencium (266) |

In your reading, you may come across the names of these elements and be unsure of how to pronounce them. This pronunciation guide will help you to say them correctly. The syllable with the capital letters is the one that you give emphasis. (For example, the word "element" would be "EL-eh-ment.") Turn back to this page whenever you need to!

Actinium: act-IN-ee-um
Americium: am-air-ISH-ee-um
Antimony: AN-teh-mo-nee
Arsenic: AR-sen-ick
Berkelium: BERK-lee-um (*though many people say* ber-KEEL-ee-um)
Beryllium: beh-RILL-ee-um
Boron: BORE-on
Cerium: SEER-ee-um
Cesium: SEE-zee-um
Curium: KYOOR-ee-um
Dysprosium: dis-PRO-zee-um
Europium: yoo-ROPE-ee-um
Fluorine: FLOR-een
Gadolinium: GAD-o-LIN-ee-um
Gallium: GAL-ee-um
Germanium: jer-MANE-ee-um
Iridium: er-RID-ee-um
Krypton: KRIP-tohn
Lawrencium: lore-EN-see-um
Lithium: LITH-ee-um
Lutetium: loo-TEE-she-um
Manganese: MANG-gan-eez (*don't confuse it with magnesium!*)
Mendelevium: men-dell-EE-vee-um
Molybdenum: moll-IB-den-um
Neodymium: NEE-o-DIM-ee-um
Palladium: pal-AID-ee-um (*or* pal-AD-ee-um)
Praseodymium: PRAZ-ee-o-DIM-ee-um
Promethium: pro-MEE-thee-um
Protactinium: PRO-tack-TIN-ee-um
Rhodium: ROE-dee-um
Rubidium: roo-BID-ee-um
Ruthenium: roo-THEE-nee-um
Samarium: sam-AIR-ee-um
Selenium: seh-LEEN-ee-um
Strontium: STRON-tee-um (*or* STRON-shee-um)
Technetium: teck-NEE-she-um
Tellurium: tell-LOOR-ee-um
Thulium: THOO-lee-um
Uranium: yu-RAIN-ee-um
Vanadium: van-AY-dee-um
Xenon: ZEE-non
Ytterbium: i-TER-bee-um
Yttrium: IT-ree-um

CHAPTER 1: WHAT IS AN ELEMENT?

Do you ever help bake things like cookies, cakes, biscuits, or bread? If so, you may have noticed that all baked goods are made from basically the same ingredients: flour, sugar, salt, eggs, butter, vegetable oil, baking powder, yeast and flavorings. The ingredients can be the same, or at least very similar, yet you have no problem telling the difference in taste and texture between pancakes and donuts, or biscuits and bread.

Even though these foods contain many of the same ingredients, the ingredients are used in different proportions. Cookies, for example, have lots of butter and sugar and not too much flour. Biscuits have less sugar than cookies do, and contain no eggs. Bread is mostly flour, with only a small amount of sugar and butter or oil (and some yeast to make it rise). Some recipes call for flavorings such as cinnamon, chocolate or lemon. The same ingredients in your kitchen can be used in many different ways to make many different foods.

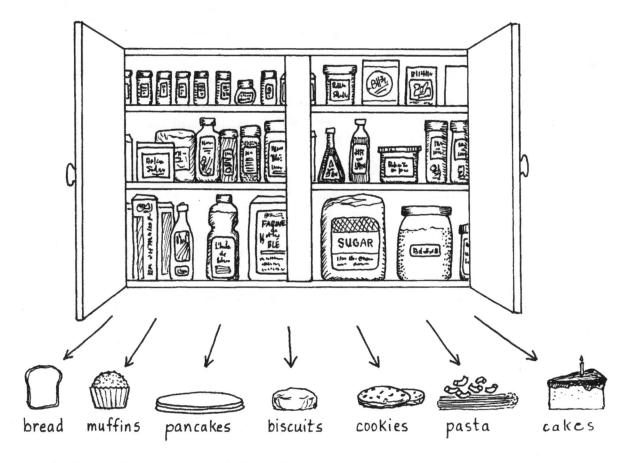

bread   muffins   pancakes   biscuits   cookies   pasta   cakes

All of these foods can be made from the ingredients in your cupboard. The reason they are different is that they have more of some things and less of others. Just a pinch of flavoring or spice can change one recipe into another. It doesn't take thousands or millions of ingredients to make a wide variety of recipes. Most of us have less than 100 ingredients in our cupboards, yet we can use them to make just about any recipe we find in a cookbook.

Activity 1.1

Use a cookbook to find the information for this activity, or ask an adult who knows a lot about cooking. For each baked good, put check marks in the boxes, showing what ingredients it contains. You are free to choose any recipes you like. (Flour means any kind, including gluten-free types. You may also cross out banana or chocolate put in something like blueberries or nuts instead.)

	flour	sugar	oil or eggs	milk or butter	water	yeast	baking powder	vanilla	banana	chocolate or other flavor
BREAD	✓	✓	✓		✓	✓				
COOKIES	✓	✓	✓	✓			✓	✓		✓
BISCUITS	✓	✓		✓			✓			
PANCAKES	✓	✓	✓	✓			✓			✓
CAKE	✓	✓	✓	✓			✓	✓		
BANANA MUFFINS	✓	✓	✓	✓			✓		✓	

Name an ingredient that is found in all of the baked goods: _flour_
Name an ingredient that is found in most of the baked goods: _oil or eggs_
Name an ingredient that is found in only one of the baked goods: _banana_

Activity 1.2

Think about cookies (tough assignment, eh?) and answer these questions:

1) How would a cookie change if you put it in the freezer? _depends on the kind_
2) How would a cookie change if you let it sit out somewhere for a week? _get stale, maybe rot_
3) How would a cookie change if you put it in a glass of water? _soggy_
4) Do these changes mean that the recipe changed? _No_
5) Do other factors, not just the recipes, contribute to the quality of foods? _yes_

We know that baked goods are made of ingredients. But what are *ingredients* made of? What is flour made of? What is water? What is oil? These baking ingredients are made of chemical ingredients called **elements**. The chemical elements are the most basic ingredients of all. They are the things that everything else is made of. There are a little over 100 chemical elements, and if we could put a sample of each into a little bottle or box, we'd have sort of a "kitchen cupboard of the universe."

These are the ingredients that make up anything you can think of: plants, animals, rocks, plastic, metal, fuel, fabric, computers, food, water, air, garbage... anything! Your body is made of these elements, too. You are a "recipe" of these chemical ingredients.

Some of these chemical elements are very common and are found in practically everything, just like flour is found in so many baked goods. You may already be familiar with the names of some of these common elements: hydrogen, carbon, nitrogen, oxygen and silicon. These five elements account for most of the matter (stuff) in the universe! Other elements are less common and have names you've never heard of, such as osmium or ruthenium. These uncommon elements are a bit like the spices lurking at the back of your cupboard— the ones you use only once in a while, such as dill weed or coriander.

Isn't it great to find out that you already know some of these elements? Another chemical element you are already familiar with is helium. You've known about that one since you were old enough to hold a balloon. You just didn't know it was one of the basic ingredients of the universe. You probably know quite a few more, too, like gold, silver, lead, iron, copper, nickel, and aluminum. How many others do you know?

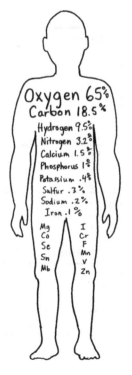

Activity 1.3   Elements you already know

How many of these elements do you recognize? Circle any name that you have heard of, even if you don't know exactly what it is. (This is not a complete list of all elements, only about half of them.)

hydrogen	helium	lithium	boron	carbon
nitrogen	oxygen	fluorine	neon	sodium
magnesium	aluminum	silicon	phosphorus	sulfur
chlorine	potassium	calcium	manganese	titanium
chromium	iron	cobalt	nickel	copper
zinc	lead	silver	gold	platinum
mercury	arsenic	selenium	tin	radon
uranium	plutonium	iodine	zirconium	tungsten

ELEMENTS IN HISTORY:

Some of these elements were familiar to ancient peoples. Silver and gold, for example, have been used for thousands of years. The ancients also knew about iron, tin, lead, copper, sulfur, and mercury. (They didn't understand what a chemical element was, however, and thought that everything was made of fire, water, earth and air.) In the 1800s, electricity was used to discover magnesium, potassium and sodium. Also in the 1800s, new elements were discovered in mines. In the 1900s, radioactive elements such as uranium and plutonium were discovered. They were named in honor of the discovery of Uranus and Pluto just a few years previously. Elements with numbers above 92 did not exist until they were artificially made in the mid-1900s.

Activity 1.4   A scavenger hunt for elements

Read the labels on some food packages or other household products and see how many elements you can find. (Pet foods are especially good choices.) Put a check mark in the box if you find that element. The names of the elements might be slightly disguised. For example, instead of sulfur you might see "sulfite," or instead of phosphorus you might see "phosphoric acid." Look for the first part of the names, and don't worry too much about the endings. The three empty spaces at the bottom are for you to add other elements that you find.

	cereal	medicine or toothpaste	bread	You choose three more:		
calcium						
carbon						
chlorine						
copper						
fluorine						
iodine						
iron						
phosphorus						
potassium						
magnesium						
zinc						

So what are *ingredients* made of? Is there a recipe to make salt or sugar? Yes, there is! The ingredients are the chemical elements and the recipes are called formulas. For example, to make salt, you need two chemical elements: sodium and chlorine. If you combine these two elements together, you will get table salt.   The recipe for sugar calls for three elements: carbon, hydrogen, and oxygen. Some chemical recipes, like sugar and salt, are fairly simple. Other materials have recipes that are extremely complicated. Livings things, such as plants and animals, are also made of chemical elements but are mixtures of so many different substances that you really can't come up with a recipe for them.

A cooking recipe looks like this:

Sugar cookies:
2 cups flour	1 egg
1/2 cup sugar	1 teaspoon vanilla
1/2 cup butter	1/2 teaspoon baking soda

Soft and chewy...
fresh from the oven!
Want one?

A chemical recipe looks like this:

glucose sugar = $C_6H_{12}O_6$

The letters are abbreviations, or **symbols**, for elements. C stands for carbon, H stands for hydrogen, and O stands for oxygen. The numbers below the letters tell you how many of each atom go into the recipe. This recipe calls for 6 atoms of carbon, 12 atoms of hydrogen and 6 atoms of oxygen. Just like with a cooking recipe, you can make a small, medium, or large batch. Theoretically, you could make a batch as small as a few molecules or large enough to fill a dump truck. As long as you keep the number of atoms in the ratio 6, 12, 6, you will get glucose sugar.

Let's look at the recipe for water:

water = H_2O

The elements in this recipe are similar to the one for glucose sugar, except that there is no carbon. You will need just hydrogen and oxygen. How much of each? There are 2 hydrogen atoms and... but there is no number after the O. Now what? If you don't see a number, it means there is only one. Scientists decided a long time ago that it was too much work to put in all the 1's in the recipes, so they agreed to just leave them out. If you don't see a number after the letter, that means there is only one. (You could think of the 1's as being invisible.)

We'll need 2 atoms of hydrogen for every 1 atom of oxygen. How much of the recipe will you make? A glass of water, or enough to fill a swimming pool? (The fascinating thing about this recipe is that when you combine two gases you get a liquid. And if you break water apart, you get two gases again.)

What about the recipe for salt?

table salt = NaCl

We don't see any numbers here at all. That means one atom of each. What are the ingredients? **Na** is the letter symbol for sodium (which used to be called natrium) and **Cl** is the abbreviation for chlorine (yes, chlorine goes in your pool, too, but it is also in salt).

Let's look at the recipe for baking soda:

baking soda = NaHCO$_3$

That's 1 atom of sodium, 1 atom of hydrogen, 1 atom of carbon, and 3 atoms of oxygen. Those are all the same ingredients we just used to make salt and sugar, but if you combine them in this proportion you will make baking soda. (Baking soda's job in kitchen recipes is to make things "puff up" in the oven.)

What else can we make with chemical elements? Here are some recipes that aren't edible:

sand: SiO$_2$ **Epsom salt: MgSO$_4$** **gold: Au** **pyrite ("fool's gold"): FeS$_2$**

We have some new elements in these recipes. **Si** is silicon, **Mg** is magnesium, **Fe** is iron, **S** is sulfur, and **Au** is gold. You can see that the recipe for gold is pretty simple—it's just the element gold with nothing added. Until the 1700s, scientists did not have a clear idea about the chemical elements. They thought that perhaps it was possible to change other materials into gold. You can see why fool's gold can never become real gold. Iron and sulfur will always be iron and sulfur.

Here is a really long recipe:

a mineral called Vesuvianite: Ca$_{10}$Mg$_2$Al$_4$(SiO$_4$)$_5$(Si$_2$O$_7$)$_2$(OH)$_4$

Wow! We won't be cooking up any of that!

* *

Activity 1.5   Making larger batches

Recipes can be doubled, tripled, or cut in half, depending upon how much of the product you want to make. See if you can figure out the answers to these recipe questions.

(Note: We're just using an imaginary "scoop" that accurately counts the atoms for us. In real life, measuring elements and mixing them requires special equipment and more difficult math.)   Answers are in answer key on page 81.

1) The recipe for the mineral calcite is CaCO$_3$. If we use 2 "scoops" of Ca (calcium), how many "scoops" of the other ingredients will we need? C = __2__   O = __6__

2) The recipe for the mineral called cinnabar (sounds delicious, but it's poisonous) is HgS. If we make a batch of cinnabar using 3 "scoops" of Hg (mercury), how many "scoops" of S (sulfur) will we need? __3__

3) You are a practical joker and want to make a batch of fool's gold to trick a friend. The recipe for fool's gold is FeS$_2$. If you use 4 "scoops" of S (sulfur) how many "scoops" of Fe (iron) will you need? __2__

4) A mineral gemstone called zircon can sometimes resemble a diamond. The recipe to make zircon is ZrSiO$_4$. If you use 2 "scoops" of Zr (zirconium), how many "scoops" of the other ingredients will you need? Si = __2__   O = __8__

Activity 1.6

See if you can match the element with the meaning of its name. (Answers are in answer key, pg. 81.)

1) Named after Alfred Nobel, inventor of dynamite and founder of the Nobel Prizes *nobelium*

2) Named after Vanadis, a goddess from Scandinavian mythology *vanadium*

3) Named after Johan Gadolin, a Finnish chemist *gadolinium*

4) Named after Poland, the country in which famous chemist Marie Curie was born *polonium*

5) Named after Albert Einstein *einsteinium*

6) Named after the city of Berkeley, California *Berkelium*

7) Named to honor our planet, Earth, but using the Greek word for Earth: "Tellus" *tellurium*

8) Named for the area of Europe called Scandinavia (Norway, Finland, Sweden, Denmark) *Scandium*

9) Named for the Swedish town of Ytterby *ytterbium*

10) Named for Niobe, a goddess in Greek mythology who was the daughter of Tantalus *niobium*

11) Named for Tinia, a mythological god of the Etruscans (in the area we now call Italy) *tin*

12) Named for Stockholm, Sweden *holmium*

13) Named in honor of the discovery of the planet Neptune *neptunium*

14) Named in honor of Marie and Pierre Curie, who discovered radium and polonium *curium*

15) Named after the Roman messenger god, Mercury, who had wings on his feet *Mercury*

16) Named after the Greek god Tantalus (father of Niobe) *tantalium*

17) Named in honor of the discovery of the asteroid Ceres *cerium*

18) Named after France, but using its ancient name, Gaul *Gallium*

19) Named after the moon, but using the Greek word for moon, "selene" *selenium*

20) Named for its really bad smell, using the Greek word "bromos" which means "stench" *bromine*

21) Named after the Latin word for rainbow, "iris," because it forms salts of various colors *iridium*

22) Named after Thor, the Norse god of thunder *thorium*

23) The name comes from the German word "Kupfernickel," meaning "Satan's copper" *nickel*

24) The name comes from the German "Kobald," a mythological gnome who lived in mines *cobalt*

25) Named for its color, yellowish-green, using the Greek word for this color: "chloros" *chlorine*

THE POSSIBLE ANSWERS: (If you need help with pronunciation, use the key before page 1.)

berkelium, bromine, cobalt, cerium, chlorine, curium, einsteinium, gadolinium, gallium, holmium, iridium, mercury, neptunium, nickel, niobium, nobelium, polonium, scandium, selenium, tantalum, tellurium, thorium, tin, vanadium, ytterbium

Just use logical reasoning to figure them out!

Activity 1.7   "The Chemical Compounds Song"

Here is a very silly song about chemical recipes. The audio tracks for this song can be found at www.ellenjmchenry.com/audio-tracks-for-the-elements (or in the zip file if you have the digital download). There are two versions of this song. The first one has the words so you can learn how they match the tune. The second version is accompaniment-only so you can sing it yourself. When singing it becomes easy, try it as a hand-clap game, like "Miss Merry Mack" or "Down, Down Baby." You don't even need the music if you use it as a hand-clap game. (Also, there is a music video of this song posted on the YouTube playlist mentioned at the top of page 17.)

The Chemical Compounds Song

Today was Mama's birthday; I tried to bake a cake.
I didn't use a recipe, that was my first mistake!

I put in lots of H_2O, 3 cups NaCl,
Some $NaHCO_3$, and other things as well.

I poured it in a non-stick pan (Teflon, C_2F_4)
I popped it in the oven (it cooks with CH_4).

I set the oven way too hot, the cake got black and charred.
Oh, why did I make birthday cake? I should have bought a card!

I had to clean and scrub the pan, so Mom would never know.
First I tried to bleach the pan with NaClO.

I needed something stronger, so I tried some HCl.
I added grit, SiO_2, and FeO, as well.

Then something awful happened, I'll never know just why.
I woke up in the hospital with stitches near my eye!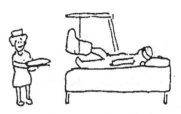

My leg was in a plaster cast of $CaSO_4$.
The nurse brought $Mg(OH)_2$ and $MgSO_4$.

Next year for Mama's birthday, I'll buy a cake, instead,
'Cause if I tried to bake again, I think I'd end up dead!

H_2O = water
NaCl = salt
$NaHCO_3$ = baking soda
C_2F_4 = Teflon
CH_4 = natural gas
NaClO = bleach

HCl = hydrochloric acid
SiO_2 = sand
FeO = a type of rust [or FeO(OH) to be more accurate] *
$CaSO_4$ = plaster
$Mg(OH)_2$ = milk of magnesia (good for intestines)
$MgSO_4$ = Epsom salt (good for skin)

* Rust is complicated. More commonly it is written as $Fe_2O_3(OH)$ or $Fe_2O_3 \cdot nH_2O$. But those don't fit the rhyme.

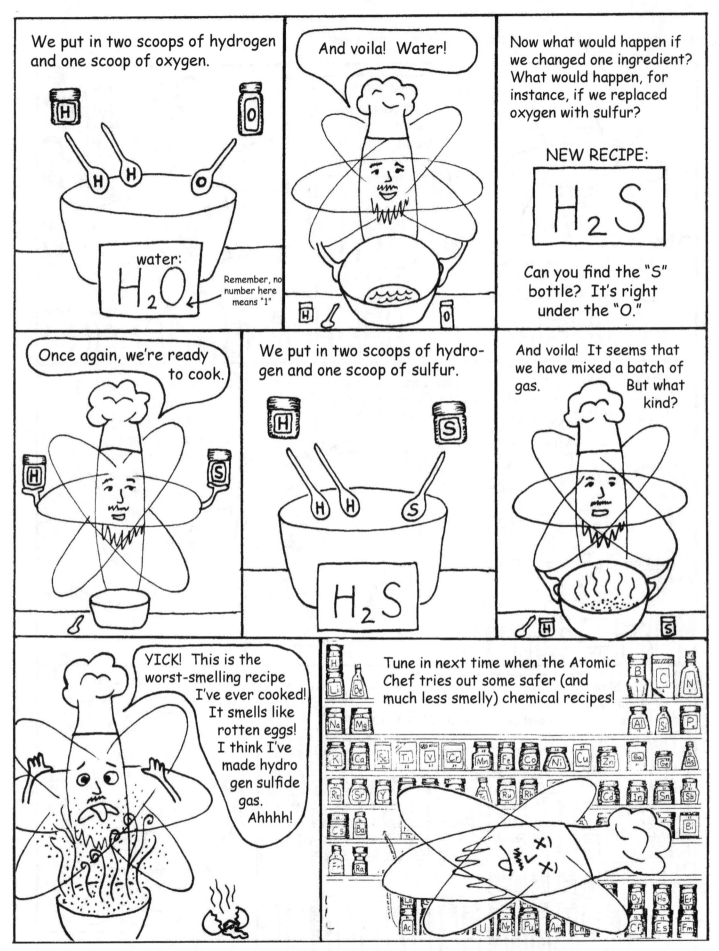

Tune in again at the end of the next chapter for more adventures with the Atomic Chef!

CHAPTER 2: THE PERIODIC TABLE

Have you ever read stories from medieval times where a person called an "alchemist" tried to make gold? The alchemists were part scientist and part magician, and although they experimented with other forms of chemistry, they are famous for trying to make gold. They boiled up mixtures of every substance they could find: copper, tin, lead, iron, coal, silver, mercury, unusual rocks, gold-colored minerals, medicinal plants, parts of animals, and anything else they could think of. They even said magic spells over their boiling pots, but they never produced a single drop of gold.

What the alchemists did not know is that gold is one of the basic ingredients in the Kitchen Cupboard of the Universe. They thought gold had a recipe like water or salt or sugar. But you can't make gold. It's a basic ingredient that comes naturally in the Earth. The letter symbol for gold is **Au**. Ancient peoples called gold by the name "aurum" and that is where we get the letters "Au." Can you find gold in the Kitchen Cupboard of the Universe?

I think if I keep trying, I MUST be able to make gold! Just because I am so determined!

ALCHEMIST

The confusion of the alchemists is very understandable. Metals don't come with labels on them telling you what they are made of. Bronze and copper were both metals. Bronze could be melted down into its two ingredients: copper and tin. The alchemists wondered why copper couldn't be boiled down into its ingredients. They didn't know that copper, like gold, is an element. It was only after years of experimenting that ancient scientists began a list of substances that they believed could not be reduced down any further. During the 300 years between 1200 AD and 1500 AD, the list of substances believed to be basic ingredients of the universe grew to include carbon, sulfur, iron, copper, silver, tin, mercury, lead, arsenic, antimony, bismuth, zinc, platinum and gold. (The alchemists eventually had to give up and admit that gold had no recipe.) All of these elements are in our kitchen cupboard of the universe, though they are not sitting all in a row.

Several hundred years went by with no new discoveries of any more basic ingredients. Then, in the 1700s, chemists really began to catch on to the idea of elements, and began intentionally looking for them. They were able to add many more substances to the list of basic elements, including hydrogen, oxygen, nitrogen, magnesium, chlorine, cobalt, nickel, bismuth, platinum and tungsten. In many cases, chemists had not yet been able to produce these substances in a pure form, but they were still pretty sure that these things were basic ingredients, not mixtures. The chemists now began calling these basic ingredients "elements," and by the year 1800, the official list of elements also included phosphorus, fluorine, barium, strontium,

Chemistry labs of the 1700s still looked a lot like the alchemists' labs of the Middle Ages.

molybdenum *(moll-IB-den-um)*, zirconium, chromium, and uranium. These elements were still very mysterious, however, and little was known about them.

The list kept growing during the 1800s, and by the middle of the century there were over 60 elements on the list. By now there was no confusion about what an element was. Scientists understood very clearly that elements were the basic ingredients of the universe. An element could not be boiled down into anything else. They also understood that there was probably a limited number of elements, and once they were all found the fun of discovery would be over. Thus, there ensued a sort of international "scavenger hunt" for new elements, with every chemist dreaming of being one of the lucky winners who would find one of the remaining unknown elements.

Amidst all this frenzy for discovering the remaining elements, a Russian chemist named Dmitri Mendeleyev *(men-dell-AY-ev)* (also spelled Mendeleev) began giving chemistry lectures at St. Petersburg University in 1867. As Mendeleyev studied in order to prepare for his lectures, he began to have the feeling that the world of chemistry was like a huge forest in which you could easily get lost. There were no trails or maps, and there were so many trees! It was all a muddled mess of elements, mixtures, oxides, salts, acids, bases, gases, liquids, crystals, metals, and so much more. The subject of chemistry was confusing to his students, and he could see why. There was no overall structure to this area of science. It was just a massive collection of facts and observations about individual substances. Each scientist had a different way  of arranging the substances, and that confused students. Some scientists grouped all the gases together, while others grouped them by color, or listed them from most to least common, or even alphabetically. Was one arrangement better than all the rest? Mendeleyev decided that he would search for some kind of overall pattern that could be applied to chemistry, making it easier for his students to learn.

Mendeleyev began by cutting 63 squares of cardboard, one for each of the elements that were known at that time. On each card he wrote the name of an element and all its characteristics: whether it was solid, liquid, or gas, what color it was, how shiny it was, how much it weighed, and how it reacted to other elements. He then laid out the cards in various ways, trying to find an overall pattern. One evening he was sitting, as usual, in front of his element cards, staring at them and trying to think of some new way to arrange them. He had been working on this puzzle for three days straight, without any sleep. Mendeleyev was exhausted as he fell asleep that night. While he slept, he dreamed about the cards. In his dream he saw the cards line up into rows and columns, creating a rectangular "table."

When he woke up, he realized that his brain had solved the problem while he had slept. The way to arrange the elements was first by weight, then by chemical properties. He began laying out the elements in order of their weight, starting with the lightest, hydrogen.

Then came helium, lithium, berylium, boron, carbon, nitrogen, oxygen, and fluorine. The next element was sodium. Instead of putting it next to fluorine, he put it underneath lithium because it had similar chemical properties to lithium. So the second line began with sodium. Then he began filling in with the elements arranged by weight again: magnesium, aluminum, silicon, phosphorus, sulfur, and chlorine. When he got to the next element, potassium, he decided to start a third line, putting potassium right underneath sodium because they had similar chemical properties. Then it was back to listing them by weight: calcium, titanium, vanadium, chromium... As he laid the cards out in order of their weight, every once in a while, or "periodically," he had to go back and start a new row so that elements that had similar chemical properties would be in the same column. This method of arranging the elements became known as the "Periodic Table" because it is a table (chart) that has patterns that repeat periodically.

This is how the main part of Mendeleyev's chart looked.

lithium	beryllium	boron	carbon	nitrogen	oxygen	fluorine
sodium	magnesium	aluminum	silicon	phosphorus	sulfur	chlorine
potassium	calcium	eka-boron	titanium	vanadium	chromium	manganese
copper	zinc	eka-aluminum	eka-silicon	arsenic	selenium	bromine
rubidium	strontium	yttrium	zirconium	columbium	molybdenum	?
silver	cadmium	indium	tin	antimony	tellurium	iodine
cesium	barium					

Mendeleyev ran into some problems with his Periodic Table. It seemed that there were awkward areas where things did not fit perfectly. He guessed that this was because there were cards missing. His set of 63 cards must be incomplete. Mendeleyev started leaving blank spaces in his chart where he believed there was a missing element. He began to predict what these elements would be like when they were discovered. He even gave them temporary names. The empty space under boron and aluminum he named "eka-boron." ("Eka" means "one more" in the Sanskrit language.) The empty space under carbon, silicon, and titanium was "eka-silicon."

Many chemists of Mendeleyev's day laughed at him for trying to predict the discovery of new elements. They did not believe in his Periodic Table and thought he was a fool for making up all these fictional elements—elements that did not even exist!

In 1875, one of Mendeleyev's predictions came true. A new element was discovered by a French chemist with a long name: Paul Emile Lecoq de Boisdaubran. He had decided to name this new element after his country, France, but using a very old word for France: Gall. He named the element "gallium." Mendeleyev listened to the description of this new element and proudly announced that gallium was, in fact, the missing element he had called eka-aluminum. Mendeleyev had already known what this element would be like. It would be a soft, silvery-blue metal with a very low melting point—so low that this metal might even melt in your hand. This is exactly how Boisdaubran described gallium. Some chemists thought this was just a coincidence and waited to see if any more of Mendeleyev's predictions would come true.

Gallium, from Wikipedia, credit for photo: en:user:foobar

After the discovery of gallium, Mendeleyev became braver about making predictions. He announced that sometime soon a scientist would discover a new element that would be a dark gray metal with a weight that was 72 times heavier than hydrogen, a specific gravity of about 5.5, and having the ability to combine with oxygen to make oxide compounds that are very hard to melt even in a hot fire. Fifteen years after this prediction, a scientist in Germany discovered a new metal that he named "germanium" (after Germany, of course). As you might guess, the characteristics of this new metal were exactly what Mendeleyev had predicted! The scientific world was stunned as they compared Mendeleyev's predictions with the actual experimental results for this new metal—they were almost identical. Germanium was Mendeleyev's "eka-silicon." Mendeleyev was happy to have a real name for "eka-silicon" and gladly replaced it with "germanium."

Germanium looks a lot like gallium. (Photo credit: wikipedia article on germanium.)

Eventually, Mendeleyev and his Periodic Table became famous all over the world. He received gold medals and honorary degrees from universities in other countries, and was invited to join important scientific societies. Sadly, however, his homeland of Russia refused to acknowledge him. When his name was presented to the Russian Academy of Sciences he was rejected. Mendeleyev was unpopular in Russia because he said things the Russian government did not want to hear. He told them they needed to be careful with Russia's supply of crude oil because it was a precious resource and would not last forever. He said that Russia's technology was lagging behind that of other nations and they needed to catch up. Sadly, the government didn't really care about improving the country, and they ingnored Mendeleyev's advice.

After Mendeleyev, chemists continued to discover elements. Every time a new element was discovered it was added to the Periodic Table. The number of elements grew from 63 to over 100. Some adjustments had to be made to Mendeleyev's original table in order to accommodate all the new discoveries. They added a middle section, plus two rows at the bottom.

Mendeleyev's table:

Reihen	Gruppe I. — R'O	Gruppe II. — RO	Gruppe III. — R'O³	Gruppe IV. RH⁴ — RO²	Gruppe V. RH³ — R'O⁵	Gruppe VI. RH² — RO³	Gruppe VII. RH — R'O⁷	Gruppe VIII. — RO⁴
1		H=1						
2	Li=7	Be=9,4	B=11	C=12	N=14	O=16	F=19	
3	Na=23	Mg=24	Al=27,3	Si=28	P=31	S=32	Cl=35,5	
4	K=39	Ca=40	—=44	Ti=48	V=51	Cr=52	Mn=55	Fe=56, Co=59, Ni=59, Cu=63.
5	(Cu=63)	Zn=65	—=68	—=72	As=75	Se=78	Br=80	
6	Rb=86	Sr=87	?Yt=88	Zr=90	Nb=94	Mo=96	—=100	Ru=104, Rh=104, Pd=106, Ag=108.
7	(Ag=108)	Cd=112	In=113	Sn=118	Sb=122	Te=125	J=127	
8	Cs=133	Ba=137	?Di=138	?Ce=140	—	—	—	— — —
9	(—)							
10	—	—	?Er=178	?La=180	Ta=182	W=184	—	Os=195, Ir=197, Pt=198, Au=199.
11	(Au=199)	Hg=200	Tl=204	Pb=207	Bi=208	—	—	
12	—	—	—	Th=231		U=240	—	— — —

The Periodic Table as it looks today:

Periodic Table of the Elements

GROUP IA	IIA	IIIB	IVB	VB	VIB	VIIB		VIIIA		IB	IIB	IIIA	IVA	VA	VIA	VIIA	VIII
1 H																	2 He
3 Li	4 Be											5 B	6 C	7 N	8 O	9 F	10 Ne
11 Na	12 Mg											13 Al	14 Si	15 P	16 S	17 Cl	18 Ar
19 K	20 Ca	21 Sc	22 Ti	23 V	24 Cr	25 Mn	26 Fe	27 Co	28 Ni	29 Cu	30 Zn	31 Ga	32 Ge	33 As	34 Se	35 Br	36 Kr
37 Rb	38 Sr	39 Y	40 Zr	41 Nb	42 Mo	43 Tc	44 Ru	45 Rh	46 Pd	47 Ag	48 Cd	49 In	50 Sn	51 Sb	52 Te	53 I	54 Xe
55 Cs	56 Ba		72 Hf	73 Ta	74 W	75 Re	76 Os	77 Ir	78 Pt	79 Au	80 Hg	81 Tl	82 Pb	83 Bi	84 Po	85 At	86 Rn
87 Fr	88 Ra		104 Rf	105 Db	106 Sg	107 Bh	108 Hs	109 Mt	110 Uun	111 Uuu	112 Uub						

57 La	58 Ce	59 Pr	60 Nd	61 Pm	62 Sm	63 Eu	64 Gd	65 Tb	66 Dy	67 Ho	68 Er	69 Tm	70 Yb	71 Lu
89 Ac	90 Th	91 Pa	92 U	93 Np	94 Pu	95 Am	96 Cm	97 Bk	98 Cf	99 Es	100 Fm	101 Md	102 No	103 Lr

It looks kind of boring to me.

Yeah, but this is just a black and white one. Wait till you see the bright-colored ones. They're beautiful!

Many decades after Mendeleyev's death, scientists realized that there was nothing on the Periodic Table to commemorate the very man who had created it. So in 1955, when a new element was discovered, the discoverers decided to honor the memory of Dmitri Mendeleyev by naming the new element "Mendelevium." It is number 101 on the Periodic Table and its letter symbol is Md.

To be fair, we really should mention that Mendeleyev wasn't the only person who saw repeating patterns in the elements. A chemist named John Newlands had noticed this in the mid 1800s and published what he called the "Law of Octaves" in 1864 (just a few years before Mendelyev's discovery). Previously, chemists had noticed groups of 3's that behaved similarly and called them "triads." (For example, lithium, sodium and potassium in the first column all reacted violently in water.) Newlands suggested that the triads were part of a larger pattern based on the number 8. He also suggested that atomic weights were a key to organizing the elements. Newlands turned out to be right about both. However, when Newlands presented his theory at the Royal Chemistry Society in London, they laughed at him and even made fun of him. They told him to go play chemistry on a piano.

Unfortunately, this type of thing happens fairly often. New theories that don't fit with current opinions are often scorned or even ridiculed. The Royal Chemistry Society did try to right this wrong in 1884 by asking Newlands to give a lecture at the Society. This time no one laughed at him. And today if you go to the Royal Society of Chemistry website, they proudly suggest that the real discoverer of the periodic arrangement of elements was British, not Russian. In fact, they've even placed a big, blue sign on his birthplace, telling all who pass by that this is where the discoverer of the Periodic Table was born.

Why did Mendeleyev get credit and Newlands did not? Mendeleyev's stroke of genius was to assume that all the elements had not been discovered, and to leave blank spots at points where the pattern seemed to fail. Newlands' table did not leave blanks for undiscovered elements, so it was bound to have problems in the end. Mendeleyev's table was not perfect, either, but it was enough better than Newlands' that Mendeleyev is remembered as the inventor of the Periodic Table.

Activity 2.1 The Periodic Jump Rope Rhyme

Use the first four rows of the Periodic Table as a jump rope rhyme. Why not? Most jump rope rhymes are pretty silly and don't make sense, anyway! The audio track will show you how to say the rhyme. Then try it on your own. If you mess up and trip over the rope, you have to start at the beginning again. Can you get to krypton? Can your friends do it?

Hydrogen, helium,
Lithium, beryllium
Boron, carbon
Nitrogen and Oxygen
Fluorine, neon

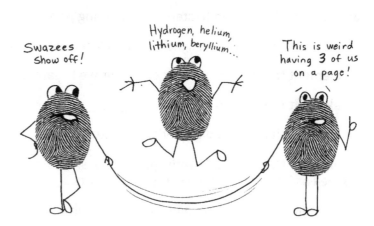

Sodium, magnesium
Aluminum and silicon
Phosphorus, sulfur
Chlorine, argon

Potassium, calcium
Scandium, titanium, vanadium, chromium, manganese!

FeCoNi's my CuZn
His last name is Gallium
He lives in Germanium
Once he ate some arsenic, thought it was selenium;
Drank it down with bromine, now he's strong as krypton!

(The audio track can be found at www.ellenjmchenry.com/audio-tracks-for-the-elements, or in the zip file if you bought the digital download version.)

Activity 2.2   What are these elements?

Use the "Quick Six" playing cards to find these elements. (Check answer key, page 81.)

1) Find an element that is used to make matches, fireworks, and detergents. _____

2) Find an element that is used in toothpaste, but is also one of the ingredients in Teflon
    (The recipe for Teflon is in the "Chemical Compounds Song.") _____

3) Find an element that is found in chalk, plaster, concrete, bones and teeth. _____

4) Find an element that is used in lasers, CD players and cell phones. _____

5) Find an element that is used to repair bones and is also used in paints. _____

6) Find an element that is found in sand, clay, lava, and quartz. _____

7) Find an element that is rose-colored and is used to make catalytic converters and headlight
    reflectors for cars. _____

8) Find an element that is used as a disinfectant for cuts and scrapes, is used to make lamps and
    photographic film, and is needed by our thyroid glands. _____

9) Find an element that is used in stadium lights and in large-screen TVs. _____

10) Find an element that is used in dentistry and jewelry, and is also used to purify hydrogen gas
    and to treat tumors. _____

11) Find an element that is an ingredient of pewter, and can also be mixed with copper to
    make bronze. _____

12) Find an element that is used to vulcanize rubber and is a component of air pollution. _____

13) Find an element that is used to sterilize swimming pools. _____

14) Find an element that is used in lightbulbs and lasers and won't bond with other elements. _____

15) Find an element that makes up most of the air we breathe. _____

16) Find an element that has no neutrons. _____

17) Find an element that makes diamonds, graphite and coal. _____

18) Find an element that is used in antiseptic eye washes but is also used to make heat-resistant
    glass, as well as being used in nuclear power plants. _____

19) Find an element that you eat in bananas but can also be used for gunpowder. _____

20) Find an element that is used in lights that need to flash brightly, such as camera flashes and
    strobe lights. _____

Activity 2.3   Watch some videos

There is a playlist for this curriculum at: www.YouTube.com/TheBasementWorkshop. Click on PLAYLISTS and then on "The Elements." (If you can't see that playlist, use the arrow on the right to scroll through each row of videos. If you still can't see it, click on the drop-down and choose "created playlists.")

It isn't possible to tag the videos to show which chapter they go with, but they are listed in order, with the chapter one videos first, the chapter two videos second, etc. There are several videos about Mendeleyev, plus a few on gallium and germanium, the elements Mendeleyev predicted correctly.

NOTE: You will notice that there is more than one way to spell Mendeleyev. Some of the videos use the spelling Mendeleev, but it is still pronounced like it has a Y between the two E's. (Recently, spelling it without the Y has become more popular, but it is harder for students to remember how to pronounce it when you don't see the Y.)

Activity 2.4   Alternative Periodic Tables

There isn't a law saying that you can't arrange the chemical elements into a shape that isn't a rectangle. Over the past century, quite a few arrangements of the elements have been proposed. They can't be printed here due to copyright restrictions, but you can easily find them online by typing "alternative Periodic Tables" in a search engine set on "images." You could look at the image gallery at the bottom of the Wikipedia article titled "Alternative Periodic Tables."

Activity 2.5   Play an online quiz game to help you learn the symbols

You can choose to play easy or harder levels, so this game is great for beginners: http://www.funbrain.com/periodic/

Check out this amazing Periodic Table! It's so large that it covers a whole wall! It is located at the Ruth Patrick Science Education Center in South Carolina. Each box in this table contains an actual sample of the element (except for the elements that are either too dangerous or too rare).

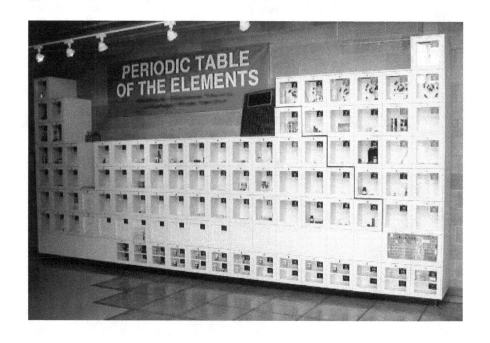

Activity 2.6

Here is a just-for-fun puzzle using the symbols (letter abbreviations) for some of the elements. Write the symbols in the blanks to make some silly riddles. (Check answer key if you need to.)

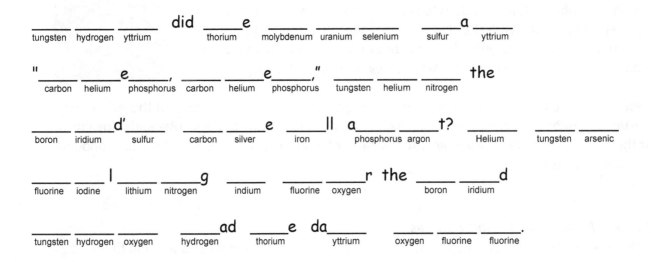

_____ _____ _____ did _____e _____ _____ _____ _____a _____
tungsten hydrogen yttrium   thorium   molybdenum uranium selenium   sulfur   yttrium

"_____ _____e_____, _____ _____e_____," _____ _____ _____ the
 carbon helium phosphorus carbon helium phosphorus   tungsten helium nitrogen

_____ _____d'_____ _____ _____e _____ll a_____ _____t? _____ _____ _____
boron iridium   sulfur   carbon silver   iron   phosphorus argon   Helium   tungsten arsenic

_____ _____l_____ _____g _____ _____ _____r the _____ _____d
fluorine iodine lithium nitrogen   indium   fluorine oxygen   boron iridium

_____ _____ _____ _____ad _____e da_____ _____ _____ _____.
tungsten hydrogen oxygen   hydrogen   thorium   yttrium   oxygen fluorine fluorine

Here's another one:

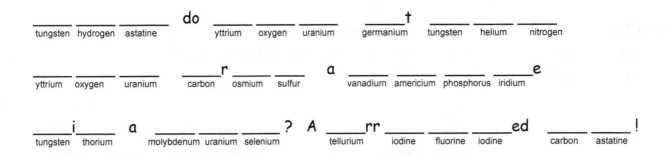

_____ _____ _____ do _____ _____ _____ _____t _____ _____ _____
tungsten hydrogen astatine   yttrium oxygen uranium   germanium   tungsten helium nitrogen

_____ _____ _____ _____r_____ _____ a _____ _____ _____ _____e
yttrium oxygen uranium   carbon osmium sulfur   vanadium americium phosphorus iridium

_____i_____ a _____ _____ _____? A _____rr _____ _____ _____ed _____ _____!
tungsten thorium   molybdenum uranium selenium   tellurium iodine fluorine iodine   carbon astatine

And one last riddle:

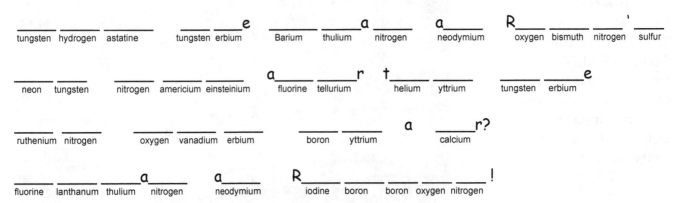

_____ _____ _____ _____ _____e _____ _____a _____ a_____ R_____ _____ '_____
tungsten hydrogen astatine   tungsten erbium   Barium thulium nitrogen   neodymium   oxygen bismuth nitrogen   sulfur

_____ _____ _____ _____ _____ a_____ _____r t_____ _____ _____ _____e
neon tungsten   nitrogen americium einsteinium   fluorine tellurium   helium yttrium   tungsten erbium

_____ _____ _____ _____ _____ a _____r?
ruthenium nitrogen   oxygen vanadium erbium   boron yttrium   calcium

_____ _____ _____a_____ a_____ R_____ _____ _____ _____ _____!
fluorine lanthanum thulium nitrogen   neodymium   iodine boron   boron oxygen nitrogen

18

CHAPTER 3: ATOMS

The scientists in Mendeleyev's day understood many things about the elements. They had even written books describing the characteristics of certain elements. However, one thing they were never able to do was examine just one particle of an element. It was not until the 1900s that scientists were able to figure out what the elements themselves were made of.

Let's open one of those ingredient jars and find out what the stuff inside looks like. How about He, helium?

ONE PARTICLE (AN ATOM) OF HELIUM:

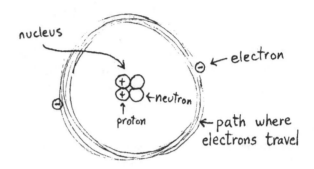

Let's look at just one of those little particles in the jar. One single particle is called an **atom**. An atom is a very strange-looking thing, and is made of up three even smaller types of particles: **protons**, **neutrons**, and **electrons**. The protons and neutrons like to hang out together in the center while the electrons go whizzing around the outside at about a million miles an hour. The central clump is called the **nucleus** of the atom, and the pathways the electrons travel in are called **orbits**, just like the pathways of the planets around the sun.

Your next question might be: "What are these particles made of?" That's a tough question, because they aren't really made of anything—they <u>are</u> the stuff that other stuff is made of. However, if you asked a physicist this question, he or she would give you a long, complicated answer that included words like "up quarks" and "down quarks." Atomic particles such as quarks are still not fully understood and require knowledge of very difficult math. (If you want to explore the world of sub-atomic particles, the Internet can help you.) All we need to know is that the proton has a postive electrical charge, the electron has a negative electrical charge, and the neutron has no charge at all. The electron is much, much smaller than either the proton or the neutron. In fact, it is so small that it adds almost nothing to the weight of the atom. When scientists figure out how much an atom weighs, they don't even bother with the electrons. They just count the protons and neutrons.

Let's open another jar.   How about Li, lithium?

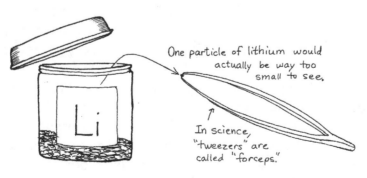

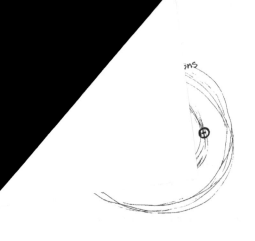

A lithium atom has three protons, three electrons, and four neutrons. The number of neutrons is often the same as the number of protons, but not always, as we see here with lithium. Smaller atoms tend to have equal, or almost equal numbers, but as the atoms get larger they begin requiring more neutrons. By the time you get to number 92, uranium, there are about 50 more neutrons than protons.

You may be wondering why the lithium atom has two rings around it instead of just one, like helium. Why isn't the third electron whizzing around in the first pathway with the other two electrons? The reason is that each ring can only hold a certain number of electrons, and although that first ring may look big enough to you, the electrons think it only has room for two of them. If a third electron comes along, the atom has to add another ring for it. The second ring is a bit bigger, and can hold up to eight electrons.

Let's look at an atom of neon. It has two completely full rings, with two in the first ring and eight in the second ring. Atoms that have full rings with no leftovers are very happy atoms. Neon is very content and good-natured. It is well-behaved and never tries to steal electrons from anyone.

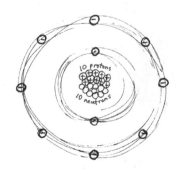

By the way, don't forget that the electrons aren't really as big as they look in these drawings. In fact... now might be a good time to discuss the dimensions of an atom.

If we were to increase the size of an atom until it reached the size of a football stadium, the nucleus would look like a marble sitting on the 50 yard line. The electrons would be smaller than the head of a pin, and they would be whizzing around the outer edge of the stadium.

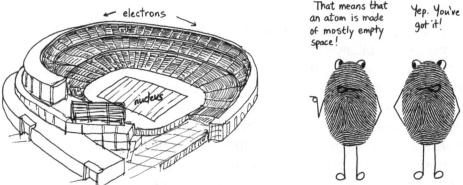

You can see why we have to draw atoms out of scale. If we drew them correctly, either you would not be able to see them, or you would have to have a book about a mile wide.

Speaking of drawing atoms, even if we could make the atoms on this page to scale, they would still be wrong. When scientists finally began to be able to "look" at atoms (though you can't look at them like you can look at a bacteria) they discovered that the electrons don't really go around the nucleus in circles. In the mid 1900s, physicists discovered that electrons move in a more random fashion, not in neat little circles like they had originally imagined. Electrons buzz around so fast that they end up looking more like a balloon than a ring. Since these balloon-like areas looked a bit fuzzy, scientists decided to call them "clouds." Drawing electrons clouds, as we will see, is not easy, which is part of the reason you still see orbitals drawn like rings in most pictures. (The correct name for the "solar system model" is actually the "Bohr model," named after physicist Neils Bohr.)

This is a rough sketch of what electron clouds look like:

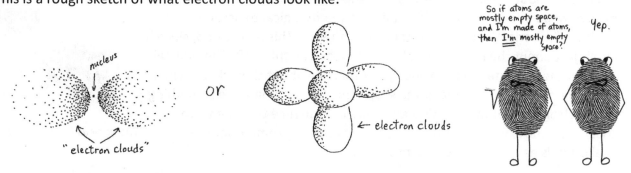

Electrons move around all the time, but they spend more time close to the nucleus than away from it. Electrons like to be in pairs, but in separate clouds on opposite sides of the nucleus. Pairs of electrons hate to be next to each other, too, so each pair will take a position as far apart from the others as possible. The result is that the clouds end up looking like a bunch of balloons tied together, with one electron per balloon.

Large atoms end up having very complicated arrangements of electron clouds and are almost impossible to draw as electron cloud models because so many of the clouds overlap in strange ways.

Activity 3.1

In this activity, you will play the part of an electron. You will map out your location every hour over a weekend. Each hour you will plot your location. For example, if you sleep for eight hours during the first night, you will put eight dots inside the center circle. The next hour might find you in the kitchen eating breakfast, so put a dot there. After that, you might spend an hour watching TV, then three hours at a ball field playing soccer. Put one dot on the TV room, and three dots on the ball field. Continue to plot your locations for several days.

When you are finished, look at your map. Where do the most dots occur? Are they spread out evenly, or is there a definite pattern to the arrangement of the dots? In this model, what represents the nucleus? Do you, the electron, spend more time near the nucleus than away from it?

NOTE: You could just remember a recent weekend (or three weekdays) and estimate the number of hours in various places.

Activity 3.2   Looking at electron cloud models

Look at some pictures of electron clouds on the Internet. Use a search engine with the key words "electron clouds." You will find many different images. Do any of the pictures look like balloons? You may see some that have hourglass shapes or ring shapes, as well as balloon shapes.

Then go to the YouTube channel for this curriculum and watch the videos that show 3-dimensional animations of electron clouds. The atoms will spin around so you can see all sides. Don't worry if there are words or letters that you don't know. Just enjoy watching the animations.

Electron clouds come in four basic arrangements. The first one is spherical in shape and is called an "s" orbital. It seems logical to assume that "s" stands for "spherical," but no... it stands for "sharp." This is very odd, since a sphere is just about the least sharp object a person can think of! The original discoverer of these orbitals was obviously not thinking about their shape when he named them. He was looking at the shape the electron made on something called a spectrograph. However, it's a fortunate coincidence that the word "spherical" also starts with the letter "s," so we can rightly remember the spherical orbitals as being the "s" orbitals.

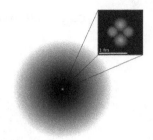

The nucleus is at the center.

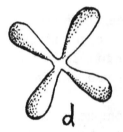

The "p" orbital looks like two balloons tied together. Its name comes from the word "principal" which means "primary" or "the main one." The "d" orbital looks like two p orbitals that were stretched out a bit then tied together. ("D" stands for "diffuse," another name we'll never remember.) The "f" orbital looks like two d's tied together. ("F" stands for "fundamental," which is curious because we already have "principal," and these two words are so similar in meaning.) These letters can be hard to remember. It would have been much easier if they had chosen "a, b, c and d."

The spherical s orbitals are always found individually, but the other orbitals are found in groups. Yes, it gets even more complicated. P orbitals are found in groups of 3, d orbitals are found in groups of 5, and d orbitals are found in groups of 7. Can you imagine 7 of those f orbitals shown above, all grouped together?

The p orbitals are found in groups of 3, looking like 6 balloons tied together. The d orbitals are found in groups of 5, and since each orbital has 4 lobes, a balloon model would have to have 20 balloons tied together. F orbitals come in groups of 7. How many balloons for this model? 8 (lobes) x 7 = 56!

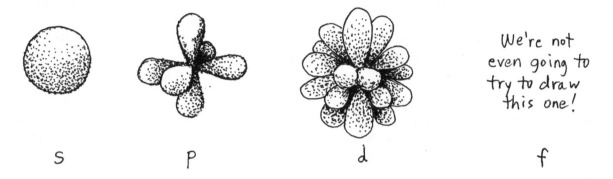

We're not even going to try to draw this one!

s   p   d   f

As you can see, this method of drawing orbitals is not easy. If we go back to using the solar system (Bohr) model, things become easier again:

The central clump is the nucleus with the protons and neutrons in it. The dots on the rings are the electrons. Still a bit complicated, but not as bad as the electron clouds. However, this model has its own problems. Most of those rings represent a combination of several electron neighborhoods (orbitals). For example, the second ring out from the nucleus represents an s neighborhood AND a p neighborhood. S orbitals can only hold 2 electrons, and p orbitals hold 6. That second ring has 8 dots on it, so it combines the s and p orbitals into one ring. These rings are often called "shells." The difference between orbitals and shells is often a major source of confusion for chemistry students.

Wouldn't it be nice if there was a way to combine these two methods, the electron clouds and the solar system model? It would clear up all the confusion about orbitals and shells. Fortunately, there IS a way to combine them, and you are just lucky enough to be using the book that invented it!

Activity 3.3   The Quick-and-Easy "Atom-izer"
Here is a very helpful invention for chemistry students: the Quick-and-Easy "Atom-izer." It lets you "build" atoms so that you can see the electron clouds while using the solar system model. You will find the Atom-izer sheet on the next page, complete with instructions on how to use it. You will need a supply of some kind of tokens that will represent electrons. You could use pennies or pieces of paper, or you might want to add some extra fun by using something edible such as mini-marshmallows or raisins or nuts, so that you can eat each atom you build.

SIDE NOTE: To avoid any scientific confusion, the word "atomizer" is also used to describe a simple device that turns liquids into a spray mist (such as an old-fashioned perfume bottle). We know this, but the name "Atom-izer" just sounded too good to pass up. It sounded like a good name for a device that makes atoms.

Look at the center of the Atom-izer. You will see a dark spot with the letter N on it. This spot will represent the nucleus of our atoms. We know that the nucleus has both protons and neutrons in it, but for this activity we are going to ignore the nucleus. Sorry, nucleus. You'll have to sit out this activity. This is all about electrons and their neighborhoods.

The rules for placing your electron tokens:
1) Always fill smaller rings before larger rings.
2) Always fill "s" orbitals first, before "p" orbitals.

Let's start with the first element: hydrogen. Hydrogen has only one electron. Place a token on one of the black squares in the first ring. It doesn't matter which you choose. Notice that the black squares are not only on the first ring, but they are also on spherical s orbitals. Once you have placed this token, you have made a model of the hydrogen atom.

Now let's make the next element, helium. Helium is number 2 on the Periodic Table and it has 2 electrons. Place a token on the other black square in the first ring. Now you have 2 electrons in the first ring, one on each s.

The next element is number 3 on the Table: lithium. Lithium has three electrons, so you will need to place a third electron token. The first ring is already full, so you will have to go to the second ring. Remember, though, in this second ring you must fill both s spots first. Place a token on either one of the s orbitals. You now have a model of lithium.

Element number 4 is beryllium *(burr-RILL-ee-um)*. It has 4 electrons. Place another token in the other s orbital in the second ring. Presto—you have beryllium!

Boron, element number 5, has 5 electrons. Since the s orbitals in the second ring are now full, you may put your token on one of the black squares on a p orbital. It doesn't matter which p you choose.

Carbon is next. It has 6 electrons, so you will need to add another token to another porbital. It doesn't really matter which you choose, but if you want to be extra-correct, place it in the p that is farthest away from the first p token you placed when you did boron. You see, electrons really don't like to be next to each other unless they have no choice. Given a choice, they will spread out and stay away from each other. So it is best to put the electrons opposite each other.

After carbon comes nitrogen. It has 7 electrons. Add another token to one of the p orbitals. This electron is going to have to be slightly close to another electron. Tough life.

To make number 8, oxygen, add another token to the second ring. To make the electrons as happy as possible, put it opposite electron number 7. Then add a 9th token to make fluorine, and a 10th token to make neon. (By this point, those electrons have no choice but to be next to each other!) Now we have a full second ring. Atoms love to have their rings full. Neon is a lucky atom.

When we go to make sodium, number 11, we will need to put the 11th electron in the third ring. But don't forget—fill those s orbitals first!

Keep adding electron tokens to make magnesium, aluminum, silicon, phosphorus, sulfur, chlorine, and argon.

What if you wanted to go on to element number 19, potassium? You would have to add a fourth ring to this chart. For now, we are going to stop at 18, argon.

Why don't you practice making some atoms "from scratch"? Clear the board, choose any atom from 1 to 18, and build it one electron at time. Then clear it, and try another one.

NOTE: If you need to print out a few extra copies of the Atomizer and you have only a paperback copy, you can download a digital file to print out by going to www.ellenjmchenry.com, clicking on FREE DOWNLOADS, then on CHEMISTRY. You will see a link for "Printable pages for The Elements curriculum."

THE QUICK-AND-EASY "ATOM-IZER"

The rules for placing your electron tokens:

1) Always fill smaller rings before larger rings.
2) Always fill "s" orbitals first, before "p" orbitals.

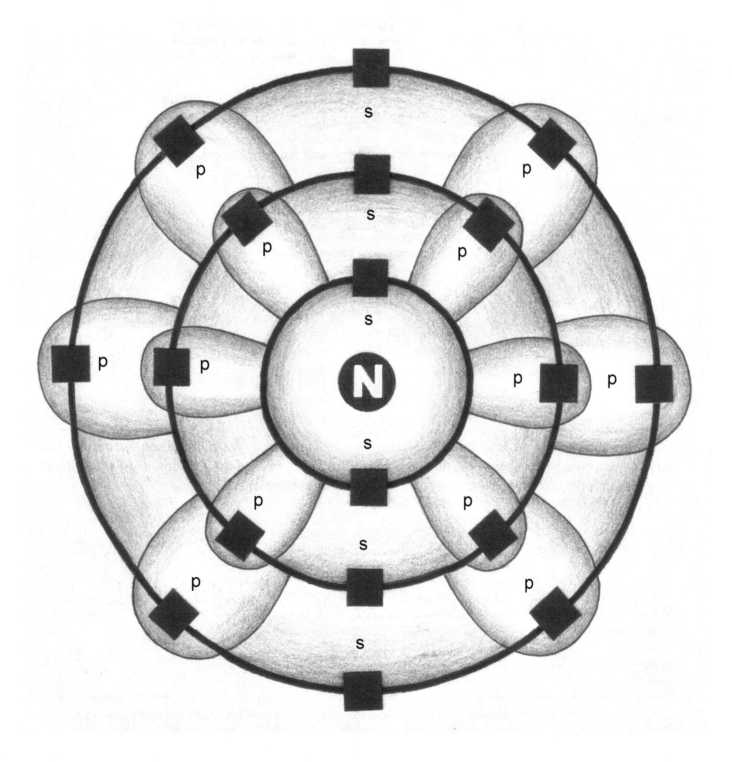

As you can see from the Atom-izer activity, drawing pictures of large atoms would be very time-consuming. So chemists decided to dispense with art altogether and use a string of letters and numbers to show which orbital neighborhoods the atom has, and how many electrons are in each. Their method looks like this: $1s^2 2s^2 2p^6 3s^2$

Look how much space it saves! It's very compact. It means exactly the same thing as a drawing with a whole bunch of rings. Let's look at this method close-up.

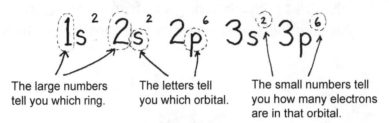

The large numbers tell you which ring.

The letters tell you which orbital.

The small numbers tell you how many electrons are in that orbital.

You can use this method exactly the same way you use the Atom-izer. Instead of the picture with the rings, just fill in the correct number of electrons in each square.

The number of electrons in that orbital goes here.

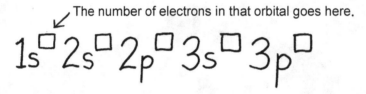

Here is the way chemists would draw oxygen and aluminum:

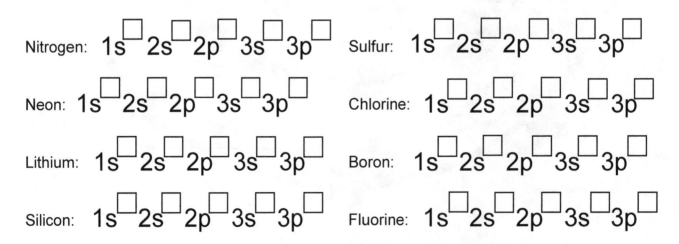

OXYGEN $1s^{\boxed{2}} 2s^{\boxed{2}} 2p^{\boxed{4}} 3s^{\square} 3p^{\square}$

ALUMINUM $1s^{\boxed{2}} 2s^{\boxed{2}} 2p^{\boxed{6}} 3s^{\boxed{2}} 3p^{\boxed{1}}$

Activity 3.4

Can you switch over from the Atom-izer to this new notation? We've listed some atoms for you to try. All you have to do is write the number of electrons, instead of placing tokens. (You know about the answer key now. It's there if you need it for the rest of the book.)

Nitrogen: $1s^{\square} 2s^{\square} 2p^{\square} 3s^{\square} 3p^{\square}$ Sulfur: $1s^{\square} 2s^{\square} 2p^{\square} 3s^{\square} 3p^{\square}$

Neon: $1s^{\square} 2s^{\square} 2p^{\square} 3s^{\square} 3p^{\square}$ Chlorine: $1s^{\square} 2s^{\square} 2p^{\square} 3s^{\square} 3p^{\square}$

Lithium: $1s^{\square} 2s^{\square} 2p^{\square} 3s^{\square} 3p^{\square}$ Boron: $1s^{\square} 2s^{\square} 2p^{\square} 3s^{\square} 3p^{\square}$

Silicon: $1s^{\square} 2s^{\square} 2p^{\square} 3s^{\square} 3p^{\square}$ Fluorine: $1s^{\square} 2s^{\square} 2p^{\square} 3s^{\square} 3p^{\square}$

Now for a very cool chemistry fact. The Periodic Table itself can be your guide to electron orbitals. If we were to circle the elements with similar electron orbitals, it would look like this:

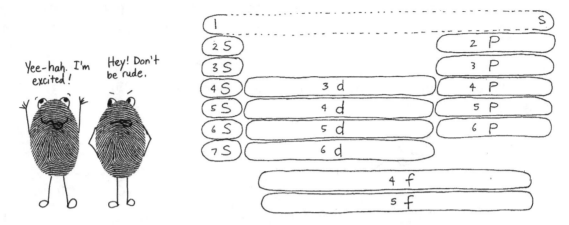

Yee-hah. I'm excited!   Hey! Don't be rude.

Changing the subject a bit, you may have noticed (during the Atom-izer activity) that the number of electrons seems to correlate with the atom's atomic number on the Periodic Table. This is, indeed, the case, but for a different reason. An atom's atomic number is determined by how many <u>protons</u> it has, not electrons. Each type of atom has a unique number of protons. For example, gold is number 79 on the Table. That means it has 79 protons. Gold is the only type of atom that has 79 protons. If you find an atom that has 79 protons in the nucleus, it's gold. If you added a proton to gold (or took one away) it wouldn't be gold any more. (Such a shame the alchemists didn't know this!)

Since atoms need to be electrically balanced with an equal number of positive and negative charges, they need to have the same number of electrons and protons. This works out nicely for chemists, because they are counting electrons all the time. It's very easy to just look at the Periodic Table for the atomic number and know that not only is it the number of protons, it is also the number of electrons. (Having said this, atoms get out of balance a lot and very often have more or less electrons than protons. We'll see this happen in future chapters.)

Activity 3.5   How many protons?

For each of the following elements, write how may protons it has in its nucleus. (Hint: Remember that the atomic number is defined as the number of protons an element has.)

Ag- silver ____   H- hydrogen ____   Os- osmium ____
Am- americium ____   He- helium ____   P- phosphorus____
At- astatine ____   I- iodine ____   S- sulfur ____
As- arsenic ____   In-indium ____   Se- selenium ____

This is a no-brainer!

Activity 3.6   Guess the atom

This is sort of activity 3.4 in reverse. Can you look at these electron configurations and determine what atoms they are? (Hint: The number of electrons is the same as the number of protons, and the number of protons is the atomic number.)

1) $1s^2\ 2s^2$ _____   2) $1s^2\ 2s^2\ 2p^3$ _____
3) $1s^2\ 2s^2\ 2p^6\ 3s^1$ _____   4) $1s^2\ 2s^2\ 2p^6\ 3s^2\ 3p^4$ _____
5) $1s^2\ 2s^2\ 2p^6\ 3s^2\ 3p^3$ _____   6) $1s^2\ 2s^2\ 2p^6\ 3s^2\ 3p^6\ 4s^2$ _____
CHALLENGE: $1s^2\ 2s^2\ 2p^6\ 3s^2\ 3p^6\ 3d^6\ 4s^2$ _____   (looking at the chart at the top of this page might help)

Activity 3.7   Time to review!

Use the symbol clues to write in the names of the elements.

ACROSS: 3) Co   6) Si   7) U   12) Cu   14) Na   13) Cr   18) Cl   20) Fe   22) O   25) P

27) Mn   28) I   30) Pu   33) Pt   36) Au   37) Ag   38) Os   39) Hg   40) Ne   41) Li

DOWN: 1) Zn   2) Rn   4) As   5) Ar   8) Ni   9) Kr   10) Mo   11) S   13) Ca   15) Xe

16) W   17) B   19) H   21) Np   23) N   24) Pb   26) Be   29) F   31) Sn

32) Mg   33) K   34) Al   35) He

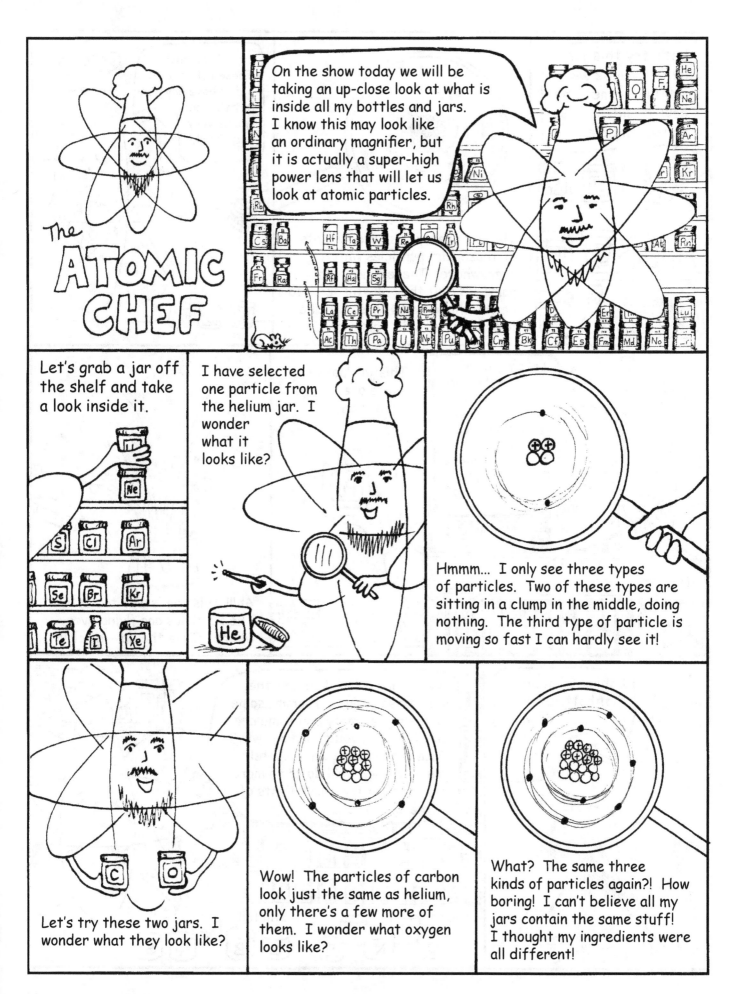

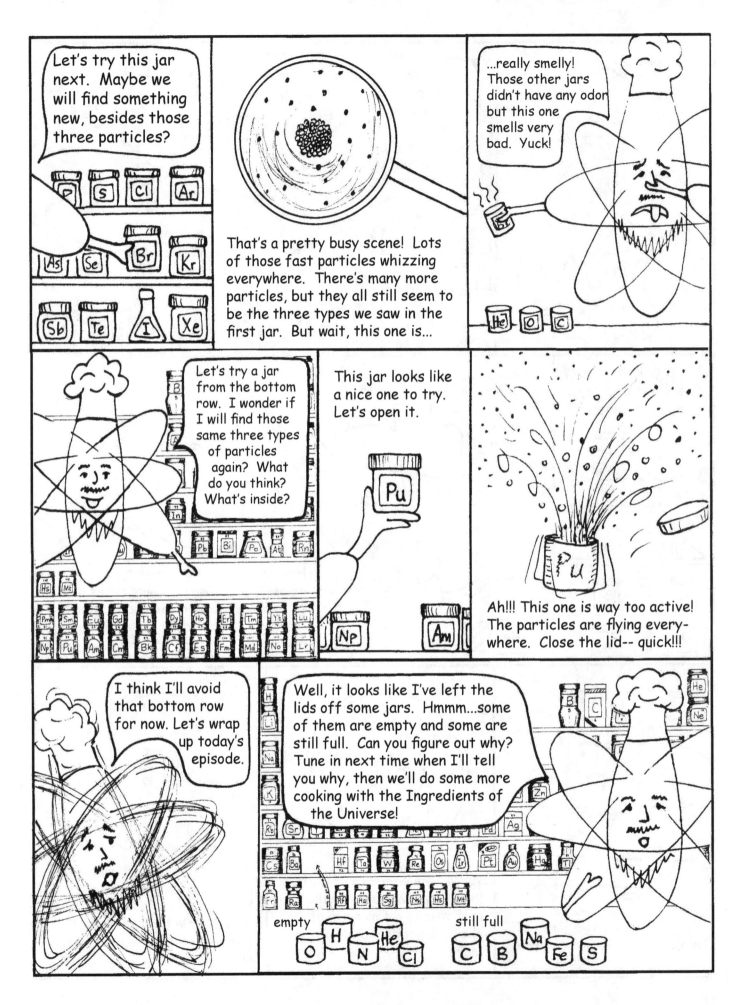

CHAPTER 4: MORE ABOUT ATOMS

We will now learn more about the incredibly interesting and wonderfully amazing subject of electrons. The reason this subject is so important is because it's the arrangement of the electrons in the orbitals (especially the ones in the outer ring) that give each element its chemical characteristics. You can suck helium out of a balloon without hurting your lungs because of the way helium's electrons are arranged. Pure chlorine gas is poisonous because of the arrangement of its electrons. If you stick a metal fork in an electrical outlet, you'll get a shock because of the way the electrons are arranged. Carbon can form thousands of different compounds (many of them organic, living molecules) because of the arrangement of its electrons. Understanding the electrons is the key to understanding the chemistry of every substance.

Here are the basic rules that electrons live by:

1) **Spin!**
2) **Always try to pair up with someone of the opposite spin.**
3) **Get plenty of privacy—stay away from other electron couples!**
4) **Try to live in a perfect neighborhood, which is often a group of 8.**

These rules were discovered by combining very complicated mathematics with high-tech scientific experiments. It's kind of funny that the rules sound so simple and yet are based on very complicated math and physics. These four rules are the key to understanding many aspects of basic chemistry.

Chemists often refer to the rings of electrons in those solar system (Bohr) models as "shells." It is the outermost shell (ring) that interacts with the environment around the atom. The electrons in the inner shells just sit there. They almost never come into contact with other atoms. The outer shell is where all the action is.

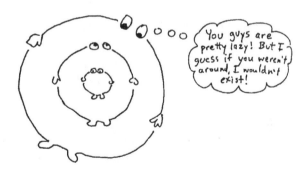

The most important thing to know about outer shells is that the electrons in them take rule #4 very seriously. They are almost neurotic about it. Atoms in the first three rows of the Periodic Table live by the motto: "8 is great!" If there is only one electron in the outer shell, that electron is so miserable that it would rather go off and join another atom than be alone in the outer shell of its own atom. If an outer shell has seven electrons, which is just one short of perfection ("8 is great!"), those seven will try anything to get an eighth electron in the shell. They will even try to steal an electron from the outer shell of any atom that comes close enough. Even when there are two electrons in the outer shell, the electrons are still not very happy. You'd think that they would be content because they have an electron buddy to form a pair with, but those two electrons are still lonely and will look to join with six others to form an "octet." ("8 is great" is often called "the octet rule.")

The number of electrons that an outer shell wants to get (or wants to get rid of) in order to have a full outer shell is called the **valence** number. If the atom needs more electrons, we say that it is minus that number, and we use a minus sign (-). For example, an atom that has seven electrons in its outer shell and only needs one more to make eight has a valence of -1. If it has six in its outer shell, and therefore would like two more, it has a valence of -2.

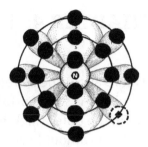

Chlorine
has 1 empty space.

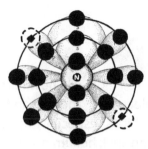

Sulfur
has 2 empty spaces.

If an atom has only one electron in its outer shell, its chances of finding seven more are pretty low. One or two, maybe... but seven? The atom gives up. It's a lot easier just to get rid of that one electron. We would say that this atom has a valence of +1. It has one to give away. Once it gets rid of that electron, the outer shell will then be empty, thus making the next shell down (which is full) the new outer shell. An atom like this can really be obnoxious. It is so desperate to get rid of that one extra electron that it will throw it at any atom that is nearby. (Chemists say "very reactive" instead of "obnoxious.") All of the elements in the first column on the Periodic Table have one extra to give away, so they are all extremely reactive.

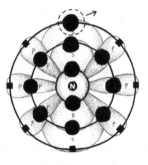

Sodium
has 1 to give away.

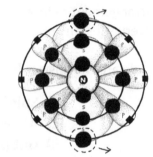

Magnesium
wouldn't mind giving 2.

What about if the outer shell has four electrons? Would the atom try to get four more, or would it give away the four it has? In this case, the atom wouldn't really give or take in the way that sodium and chlorine do. It would be more accurate to say that it forms four bonds, and leave it at that. If an atom has four electrons in its outer shell, we would say that it has a valence of plus or minus four: ± 4. Carbon and silicon are good examples.

You may be wondering if there are any completely happy atoms out there. Yes, there are six incredibly lucky elements on the Periodic Table. Their outer shells are full and they are happy; they are completely non-reactive. These lucky atoms are called the "noble gases." You can find them in the very last column on the right. They are helium, neon, argon, krypton, xenon and radon.

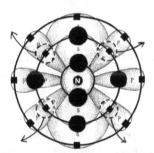

Carbon
has a valence of ± 4

You are very familiar with helium, and you've certainly heard of neon lights. You probably know that Superman is killed by kryptonite, which is a completely fictional substance made up by the cartoonists, and has nothing to do with krypton. Krypton, argon and xenon are used in very bright light bulbs, such as camera flashes. Radon is famous for lurking in basements and causing health problems because of its radioactivity. (Radon's radioactivity isn't an issue with its electrons.) These noble gases have a valence number of 0 because they don't want any electrons and they don't have any to give away. They are perfectly content. Why are they called "noble" gases? They aren't royal, of course. However, if you give human personalities to atoms and say that stealing electrons is bad behavior, then these gases certainly are noble in that they stay out of fights and squabbles over electrons.

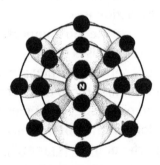

Argon
is perfectly happy.

Activity 4.1   Determining valence numbers

Determine the valence number of these atoms. We've drawn only the outer electron shell because you don't need to see the inner ones to figure out the valence. Remember, the valence is the number of electrons an atom wants to get, or to give away, in order to have 8 in the outer shell. (Remember rule #4: "8 is great!") (+) means extras to get rid of, and (-) means empty spaces to fill. Choose the smaller number as the valence. For example, if you have a choice between a valence of +6 or -2, choose -2 because 2 is less than 6.

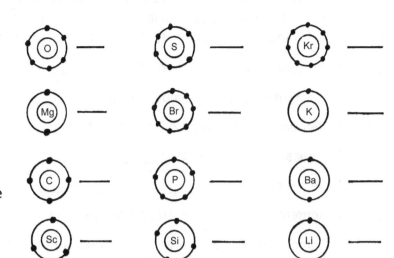

Activity 4.2   Lewis dot diagrams

We don't even need to draw those rings in order to show the valence electrons. (Scientists find all kinds of short-cuts!) All you need to do is write the letter symbol for the atom, then put electron dots around it, with a maximum of two per side (top, bottom, left, right). This is called a Lewis dot diagram.

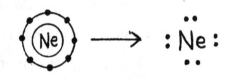

Look at the Lewis dot diagrams and figure out the atom's valence number. This is almost exactly what you did in the previous activity. The only difference is that there are no rings, just electron dots.

B: ＿＿   ·P: ＿＿   ·Ö: ＿＿   H· ＿＿

·S̈: ＿＿   Mg: ＿＿   Äl: ＿＿   Li· ＿＿

:Ne: ＿＿   ·C̈: ＿＿   ·N̈: ＿＿   :F̈l: ＿＿

Now it's your turn to be the artist and draw the Lewis dot diagrams. Each atom is listed with its valence number. Draw the diagram for each.

Li (lithium) +1 ＿＿＿＿

C (carbon) +4 ＿＿＿＿＿

B (boron) +3 ＿＿＿＿

Be (beryllium) +2 ＿＿＿＿

I (iodine) -1 ＿＿＿＿

K (potassium) +1 ＿＿＿＿

N (nitrogen) -3 ＿＿＿＿

S (sulfur) -2 ＿＿＿＿

Hey! What's going on? This is already the 3rd page of the chapter and we haven't appeared yet! What's up?!

Oh. So I've just been informed that there wasn't room for us on the first three pages. So that's what we are, eh? Nothing but space-fillers?!

Activity 4.3 Some very silly element riddles

Here are some totally silly riddles about the names of some of the elements. There is no factual information whatsoever in these riddles!   The point of this activity is just to work on memorizing the letter symbols (and have fun doing it). Fill in the name of the element in the blank.

1) Which element puts you to sleep? _____

2) Which element describes an empty cookie jar? _____

3) Which element describes what dogs do with bones? _____

4) Which is the smartest element? _____

5) Which element is "far out"? _____

6) Which element speaks Spanish, French and German? _____

7) Which element do you need when your clothes are wrinkled? _____

8) Which element is Superman's least favorite? _____

9) Which element has wings on its feet? _____

10) Which element cheers for the Los Angeles Dodgers? _____

11) Which element went to a Clown Convention? _____

12) Which element is found in your wallet? _____

13) Which element plays an equestrian sport? _____

14) Which element is Dorothy's favorite? (The scarecrow and tin man also like it.) _____

Possible answers:

Es	Ni	B	Eu	Po	Cf	Kr
Ba	Ar	Si	Hg	Fe	Pu	Os

Activity 4.4   An on-line game   (https://phet.colorado.edu/en/simulation/build-an-atom)

The University of Colorado has a webpage that is very helpful for practicing all those numbers on the Periodic Table. First, there's the atomic number, which is the official number of each element and is the number of protons it has. This is very important to remember. The number of protons determines what element an atom is. Then there's the atomic mass number, which is the combined "weight" of all the protons and neutrons in the nucleus. Protons and neutrons have a mass ("weight") of "1." You can figure out how many neutrons are in an atom by subtracting the number of protons from the mass number. However, you'll notice that the atomic mass numbers are often complicated numbers with decimal points. This is because they are averaging the weights of millions of atoms of that element, and here and there you'll find a few atoms that have one more or one less neutron than most. So these "oddballs" have to be figured into the average weight. For atomic weight, just use the closest whole number. Finally, there are the plus and minus signs which signify ions. Add or subtract electrons and see how the electrical balance signs change. You'll get the hang of it!

Okay, now back to serious business...

Let's look at another pattern on the Periodic Table. Here is the Table with only the valence numbers written in. See if you can find a pattern. (It's pretty obvious.)

																	0
+1	+2											+3	±4	-3	-2	-1	0
+1	+2											+3	±4	-3	-2	-1	0
+1	+2	+3	+4	+5	+6	+7	+3	+3	+3	+2	+2	+3	±4	-3	-2	-1	0
+1	+2	+3	+4	+5	+6	+7	+3	+3	+4	+1	+2	+3	±4	-3	-2	-1	0
+1	+2	+3	+4	+5	+6	+7	+3	+4	+4	+3	+2	+3	±4	+5	-2	-1	0
+1	+2	+3	+4														

*NOTE: Many elements have more than one valency (or "oxidation state"). For example, arsenic can be +3, -3, or +5. We chose -3 in order to emphasize the pattern.

For the most part, the elements in a column have the same valence number. Some elements do, however, have more than one valence, especially the elements in the middle of the table, so we had to simplify the table a bit. Only one valence number was chosen for each element so that the pattern would be more obvious. Chemistry is always like this—things that are generally true, but with lots of exceptions. In this book, we are emphasizing the things that are generally true.

This pattern is more than just an interesting mathematical curiosity. Think back to the story of Dmitri Mendeleyev. Do you remember that Mendeleyev could predict what unknown elements were going to be like before they were discovered? He did not know about valence numbers, but he did know that all the elements in a column were strikingly similar. All would react, or not react, with the same substances. All would have similar electrical properties. Although not identical, they would have similarities in color or texture. Mendeleyev found that if he knew the characteristics of the element at the top of a column, he could predict what the elements below it would be like.

These observations about similarities between elements eventually led chemists to divide up the elements into "family groups." Unfortunately, the names of the families are not anything interesting or easy. They sound like chemistry names. The worst thing is that the first two have very similar names, so it is easy to get them confused.

Alkali Metals
Alkali Earth Metals
Transition Metals
Metals
Semi-metals
Non-metals
Noble Gases
Lanthanide Series
Actinide Series

Notice how many "metals" there are. About 85% of all elements are classified as metals. Sodium doesn't seem like a metal since we most often meet it as a component of table salt. Yet when it is isolated, pure sodium looks like a hard, shiny lump. If you'd like to see what the elements look like in their pure form, use an image search with key words "Theodore Gray Periodic Table."

Activity 4.5   Finding the "families" on the Periodic Table

Use the symbol code shown next to each element to color each square. Color lightly so you can still see the letters and numbers. Or, you may want to just trace around the inside of each square with color. You can choose any colors you want. Fill in the colors in the squares next to the family names, so you know what's what. (The unlabeled elements are the super heavy aratifical elements. Even some of the actinides are artifical, though.)

Symbol code:
- **+** Alkali metals ☐
- **∧** Alkali earth metals ☐
- **⊤** Transition metals ☐
- **X** "True" metals ☐
- **L** Lanthanide series ☐
- **□** Semi-metals ☐
- **•** Non-metals ☐
- **H** Halogens ☐
- **o** Noble gases ☐
- **A** Actinide series ☐

1 .H																	2 oHe
3 +Li	4 ∧Be											5 □B	6 .C	7 N	8 .O	9 HF	10 oNe
11 +Na	12 ∧Mg											13 xAl	14 □Si	15 P	16 .S	17 HCl	18 oAr
19 +K	20 ∧Ca	21 ⊤Sc	22 ⊤Ti	23 ⊤V	24 ⊤Cr	25 ⊤Mn	26 ⊤Fe	27 ⊤Co	28 ⊤Ni	29 ⊤Cu	30 ⊤Zn	31 xGa	32 □Ge	33 □As	34 .Se	35 HBr	36 oKr
37 +Rb	38 ∧Sr	39 ⊤Y	40 ⊤Zr	41 ⊤Nb	42 ⊤Mo	43 ⊤Tc	44 ⊤Ru	45 ⊤Rh	46 ⊤Pd	47 ⊤Ag	48 ⊤Cd	49 xIn	50 xSn	51 □Sb	52 □Te	53 HI	54 oXe
55 +Cs	56 ∧Ba	57 LLa	72 ⊤Hf	73 ⊤Ta	74 ⊤W	75 ⊤Re	76 ⊤Os	77 ⊤Ir	78 ⊤Pt	79 ⊤Au	80 ⊤Hg	81 xTl	82 xPb	83 xBi	84 □Po	85 HAt	86 oRn
87 +Fr	88 ∧Ra	89 AAc	104 Rf	105 Db	106 Sg	107 Bh	108 Hs	109 Mt	110 Ds	111 Rg	112 Cn	113 Nh	114 Fl	115 Mc	116 Lv	117 Ts	118 Og

In a future chapter we will find out why these two rows are at the bottom.

58 LCe	59 LPr	60 LNd	61 LPm	62 LSm	63 LEu	64 LGd	65 LTb	66 LDy	67 LHo	68 LEr	69 LTm	70 LYb	71 LLu
90 ATh	91 APa	92 AU	93 ANp	94 APu	95 AAm	96 ACm	97 ABk	98 ACf	99 AEs	100 AFm	101 AMd	102 ANo	103 ALr

The Periodic Kingdom

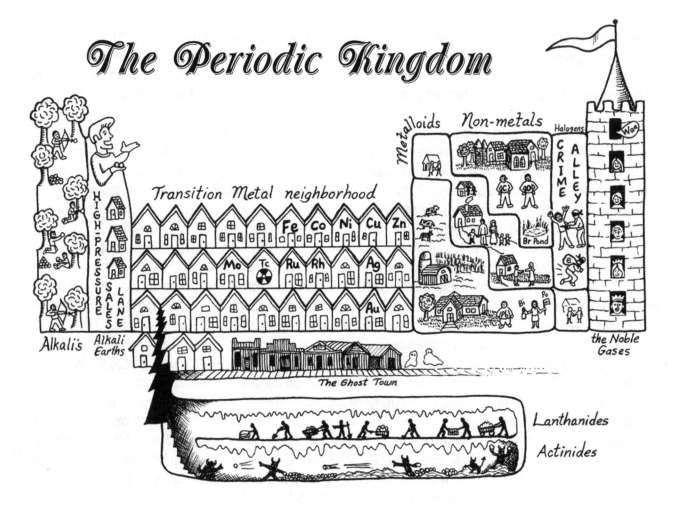

A silly story about real chemistry...

Once upon a time, in a land all around us, was the Periodic Kingdom. The royal family of the kingdom lived on the eastern shore in their tall castle tower. They were the Noble Gases: King Radon, Queen Xenon, Prince Krypton, Prince Argon, Princess Neon, and baby Helium. The Noble Gas family were the most peaceful rulers a kingdom could hope for. They never got upset and never argued with anyone. They remained calm no matter how much turmoil was going on around them.

There was one square mile of land just outside the castle. This land had been divided diagonally, split between two large families. The Metal family set up their homestead in the south western corner. The other family, who lived in the northeast, had such a long last name that no one could remember it, so they became known simply as the Non-metals. Over the years, some members of the Metal family had married members of the Non-metal family. They lived right in the middle, along the diagonal dividing line. This new family was half Metal and half Non-metal, so they became known as the Semi-metals. After several generations, one of the grandchildren decided he did not like being called a name that sounded like "half-breed" so he decided to change the family surname to Metalloid.

In general, the members of the Non-metal family were very conscientious and hard-working. (Without carbon and oxygen, for example, life on earth could not exist.) However, one section of the Non-metal family had gone bad. They all lived on the street nearest to the castle tower. The people of the kingdom called this street "Crime Alley." These poor wretches were always in need. Desperate to gain an electron, they would stop at nothing.

They would even steal or kill to get one. Ashamed to be associated with them, the Non-metals began calling them by a different name: the Halogens. Some folks say this is a sarcastic reference to a halo. Others say the name is based on a statement someone made about them not being worth their salt. Either way, stay out of their neighborhood if you know what's good for you!

Situated in the middle of the kingdom was the town, with all the honest, hard-working laborers. Many of them were miners who earned their living digging for iron, cobalt, nickel, copper and zinc. There were also craftsmen such as silversmiths and goldsmiths. Notable women of the town included Molly, Ruth and Rhoda. Between Molly and Ruth lived a mysterious neighbor who was rarely at home. The strange geometric figure posted on his door made Molly and Ruth nervous, and they told everyone to stay away from it.

On the very western edge of the kingdom lived a band of outlaws named the Alkali Brothers. These outlaws weren't the ordinary type-- they were more like Robin Hood and his band of merry men. They represented generosity gone wrong. The members of the Alkali family have an extra electron they would like to get rid of, but instead of being nice and simply offering it to the poor, they forced the poor to take it whether they wanted it or not. The Alkalis would resort even to violence, if necessary, to get a poor atom to accept an electron! Anyone who came near an Alkali was in danger of being forced to take an electron. (Except the Royals, that is. They lived an enchanted life, unaffected by any of the troubles around them.)

Some of the Alkali outlaws eventually recognized the errors of their ways, tried to reform, and moved a little closer to town. Someone said they had "come back down to Earth" (meaning that they had become more realistic about life) so they added "Earth" to their name and called themselves the Alkali Earth family. However, they still had that Alkali blood running in their veins and that made them pretty pushy. They each had two electrons to give away and they really knew how to pressure folks into taking them!

On the south side of the kingdom was the Ghost Town. The houses all sat there with names on the doors, but mostly there was never anyone home. Once in a while someone would come into town with wild tales about having seen someone in one of the houses for a split second before they disappeared into thin air.

The strangest part of the kingdom was underground. You could only get to it by way of a narrow crack between two of the streets in town. The crack led down into an underground cavern populated by two separate families: the Lanthanides and the Actinides. The Lanthanides were friendly and spent their days mining for rare metals. The Actinides were a treacherous species, and would throw radioactive hand grenades at anyone who came close enough. Beware the Actinides!

CHAPTER 5: MEET THE ALKALI AND HALOGEN FAMILIES

After reading that story, you are probably wanting to know more about these strange families. Let's start with the Alkali brothers, those Robin Hood bandits that live on the western shore of the Periodic Kingdom. When we did the Quick and Easy Atomizer, you may have noticed that lithium and sodium both had just one electron in their outer shells:

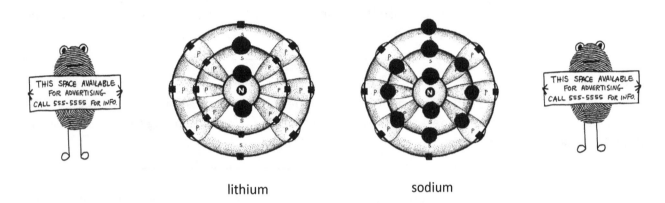

lithium   sodium

Also, you will remember that electrons really don't like to be alone. It goes against one of the rules they live by: "Pair up!" That one electron in the outer ring doesn't think it's worth being part of this atom if it has to be by itself. Therefore, it will try to get away, any chance it gets. It will even try to force itself on atoms that don't want it, which is why these guys are so dangerous. Imagine a group of atoms floating around, minding their own business, when suddenly sodium comes along and "throws" an electron at them. That unwanted electron could cause major disruption. Some substances get very upset when sodium comes near them because sodium can cause quite a reaction—combustion, in fact. If you put a piece of pure sodium into water you will get a spectacular "burning" reaction. Water burning? You might have to see it to believe it.

Activity 5.1

Go to the YouTube playlist and you'll find several vidoes that show what sodium does in water. There are also a few videos that show other alkali metals, not just sodium. The alkali metals underneath sodium are even worse!

Since all the elements in a column tend to behave in the same way, (as Mendeleyev knew quite well), we would expect that all the alkali metals would have strong reactions to water. This is true, and, in fact, the reaction gets stronger as you go down the column. Cesium is the most reactive of all. Francium is radioactive so you just don't play with that one.

Oddly enough, alkali metals almost never look like metals. If it were not for electrolysis (putting electrical wires into solutions) we would never see pure sodium, and would not know that it could look like a shiny, gray metal. When we meet sodium and potassium in the real world (not in a lab) they don't look like metals at all. They are joined together with atoms of other elements to make molecules such as salt or baking powder. As a general rule, you never, ever, meet the alkali metals by themselves. They are always in the company of other elements. Some elements like gold or silver or sulfur can be on their own, but not the alkali metals.

What about hydrogen? It's in that first column.

On many Periodic Tables, hydrogen is placed right above lithium. Hydrogen has only one electron, so it could be classified as a (+1) valence atom, like the alkali elements in the first column. Hydrogen is super reactive, just like the alkali metals, and is therefore very flammable. It's famous for exploding and burning in the Hindenburg air ship in 1937. However, hydrogen is always a gas and therefore can't be solid or shiny like a metal, so it really can't be included in the Alkali family. Some Periodic Tables choose to emphasize the uniqueness of hydrogen, and place it at the top center of the Table, all by itself, instead of in the first column. Putting hydrogen in the center, though, can create artistic problems for graphic designers who are trying to make the table look nice, so H often gets placed above Li, freeing up the center for other things.

Activity 5.2

If you would like to see the Hindenburg burning, there is a video posted in the YouTube playlist. This film was taken by a movie camera that was rolling that day in 1937, intending to record a historic flight, not a disaster. Oops.

The Halogen family, which occupies the column right outside the castle tower, has the opposite problem. They have an outer shell that is missing one electron. They are one short of a full shell and that drives them crazy. So close! They are desperate to get that one last electron to fill that shell, and will try to steal an electron from any atom that comes near. That's why pure chlorine gas is so dangerous. Chlorine atoms all by themselves make a green, poisonous gas. The reason it's poisonous is because of its dire need for an electron. Chlorine would love to find an atom that has an extra electron to give away. Hey, wait a minute—are you thinking what we're thinking? We've got one type of atom that is desperate to get rid of an electron (the alkalies) and one type of atom that is desperate to get an electron (the halogens). The answer is obvious, right? Why not pair these two up?!! Let's introduce sodium to chlorine and see what happens...

  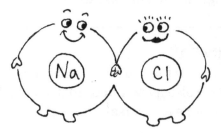

Hey, they like each other! In fact, they seem inseparable—it's a perfect match! The chlorine atom was glad to take the electron that sodium wanted to get rid of.

When two atoms join together, it's called a **molecule**. This is a molecule of NaCl. We know it as ordinary table salt. Remember, we told you that when you meet the alkali metals in real life, they don't look like metals at all. In salt, sodium definitely does not look like a metal, and chlorine doesn't look like a poisonous green gas, either. And though the two of them are dangerous by themselves, when joined together they are safe. You can eat salt and it doesn't hurt you.

The Greek word "halo" means "salt." The word halogen means salt-forming. Any time a halogen connects to an alkali metal, it forms a salt. That would mean that KCl would also be a salt, as well as KBr, LiBr, KI, NaI, CsBr, etc. Any combination of an atom from the alkali metal family with an atom from the halogen family is a salt.

Now this creates some confusion, doesn't it? When chemists talk about "salts" they are not talking about just table salt; they are talking about a whole group of molecules. However, when non-chemists talk about salt, they are usually talking about the stuff we shake onto food. That's why chemists are very careful to say "table salt" when they are talking about NaCl.

There is a special word for this type of bonding, where one atom gets rid of an electron and the other takes it. It's called **ionic bonding**. The root word is "ion." So what's an ion?

An **ion** is an atom that has an unequal number of electrons and protons. We know that an atom all by itself has to be electrically balanced, with an equal number of electrons and protons, so that the positive charges and negative charges are equal. If an atom has either more protons than electrons, or more electrons than protons, it is called an "ion." The word "ion" comes from Greek and means "going." Michael Faraday, one of the scientists who discovered electricity in the early 1800s, chose this name for these unbalanced atoms. Where are the ions going? Faraday saw them going to metal electrodes that were stuck into chemical solutions. Some ions would go over to the postive electrodes and others would go to the negative electrodes.

Let's look at the sodium and chlorine atoms while they are bonded to each other.

Here is an electron/proton count:

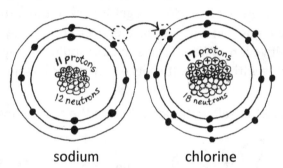

sodium   chlorine

	electrons	protons
Na (sodium)	10	11
Cl (chlorine)	18	17

Sodium has 10 negative electrons and 11 positive protons. Since negative and positive sort of cancel each other (like positive and negative numbers in math), this means that sodium has an overall electrical charge of +1. Conversely, the overall charge of chlorine is -1 because it has one more negative electron than it does positive protons.

Chemists write ions like this: Na^+ or Ca^{2+} They put the overall electrical charge in very small type (called superscript) at the top right of the letters. If the number happens to be a 1, they often leave out the 1 and just put a positive or negative sign, as though the 1 was invisible.

Since our sodium and chlorine ions now have opposite electrical charges, Na^+ and Cl^-, they are attracted to each other and the ions stick together. (Always remember: **opposites attract**.)

What makes table salt safe to eat, when sodium and chlorine are so dangerous? When sodium and chlorine are bonded together, they are both very content. Sodium no longer wants to get rid of an electron, and chlorine has the extra it wanted. Everyone is happy. Therefore, a molecule of NaCl is very safe. You can hold salt in your hand and it just sits there. If you put salt into water, though, you can get the two to separate. Once separated, the two atoms have the potential to be very dangerous again. Water, however, has a way to deal with this. Fortunately, our bodies are full of water

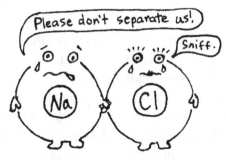

molecules, so we can safely eat salt. (In fact, sodium and chlorine ions are essential to our health!)

Activity 5.3   Tear apart salt molecules and put them back together again

For this activity you will need a hair dryer, salt, water, a bowl and two plates. If you have a magnifying lens, add this to your list, so you can get a close-up look at the crystals.

How would you go about tearing sodium away from chlorine? Use microscopic pliers? Actually, all you need to do is put them into a glass of water.   The water molecules will pull the sodium atoms away from the chlorine atoms. We call this process "dissolving."

Put some salt into the water and stir it. The salt will seem to disappear. As the sodium and chlorine molecules detach from each other, the water molecules form "cages" around them.

A water molecule looks like this.

The side with the oxygen atom has a slight negative charge and the side with the hydrogens has a slight positive charge.

The sodium ions in the lattice (the square pattern) have a positive charge. Therefore they are attracted to the oxygen atoms in the water molecules. The chlorine ions have a slight negative charge and are attracted to the hydrogens in the water molecules. Remember, sodium gave away its extra electron. It doesn't get it back in this situation. Sodium goes on without the electron, continuing on as a positive ion. Water is able to coax sodium away from chlorine without it getting its electron back again.

represents attraction

This is what salt water looks like on the atomic level:

They're in water "cages"!

Cl is negative, so the water molecules turn their postive sides towards Cl.

Na is positive, so the water molecules turn their negative sides towards Na.

Pour two puddles of salt water (about an inch in diameter), one on each plate. Make sure they are far enough apart so that you can dry one with the hair dryer without the other one being affected. Leave one puddle to evaporate on its own. Blow the other puddle with the dryer so that it evaporates quickly. What you are doing is removing water molecules.   With the water molecules gone, the sodium and chlorine atoms once again bond together. You should see crystals forming. Observe both puddles after they are completely dry. Which crystals look more like salt crystals? The ones that dried more slowly had more time to make nice crystals. The ones that were hurried with the hair dryer had to do a rush job. (Have you ever had to do something in a big hurry and felt like you could have done it a lot better if you had had more time?)

So the alkali metals love to pair up with the halogens. They give and take their electrons and are very happy together. And when they get together, the result is always a salt.

What about the "cousins" of the Alkali brothers? The ones that reformed and decided to be just pushy instead of dangerous? In our story we said that they "came back to Earth" in their attitude, so they became the Alkali Earth Metals. This isn't really the reason the word "earth" is in their name, but the story is a great way to remember their name, and it is true that they are not quite as bad as the alkali metals, but are still very insistent on giving away the two electrons in their outer shell.

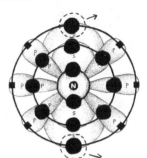

Magnesium

The most famous alkali earth metals are magnesium and calcium. How many times have you been told to drink milk because it has calcium in it? (Spinach has calcium, too!) Our bodies need both calcium and magnesium in order to work properly. Magnesium was one of the atoms you made when you did the Quick and Easy Atom-izer. Here it is, on the right, showing its two lonely electons in the outer shell. To fill the shell, it would have to find another six electrons. It's easier for magnesium just to give away those two.

Now let's think about the Periodic Table. What column on the table has atoms that would like to get two electrons? The column to the left of the halogens. This column is made of oxygen, sulfur, selenium, tellurium, and polonium. Let's try matching up magnesium with oxygen and see what happens.

The recipe for what we have made is MgO. The name for it is **magnesium oxide**. You can find this substance occurring in nature as the mineral **periclase**. This mineral can be used in a lot of ways. It is the primary ingredient in some stomach medicines that relieve heartburn. It is used in making fireproof construction materials and as insulation against electrical fires in cables. Both humans and animals can take it as a way to get magnesium in their diet. Magnesium is necessary for your body to heal itself. A magnesium compound called epsom salt can be added to warm water to make a solution to soak in. Magnesium helps both skin and muscles stay healthy.

A sample of periclase

Once again, we have **ionic bonding** going on. Whenever you have elements on the left side of the Table pairing up with elements on the far right side, you get an ionic bond (two atoms giving and taking electrons), and the result is a salt. Would magnesium be just as happy with sulfur as it is with oxygen? Yes, it would. Sulfur also needs two electrons. If you pair magnesium and sulfur you get MgS, **magnesium sulfide**. This substance doesn't have nearly as many uses as MgO. However, if you need to get rid of sulfur, magnesium is always willing to take it. During steel production, iron is heated up so hot that it becomes a liquid. Unfortunately, the molten iron has some other things mixed in with it, and sulfur is often one of them. You don't want sulfur in your iron. How do you strain out the sulfur? One way is to dump powdered magnesium into the molten iron. The magnesium will go around pulling all the sulfur atoms out of the steel. Then the magnesium and sulfur bond together and form MgS, which floats on the surface and can be raked off. Isn't that a clever use of chemistry?

Epsom salt is a combination of magnesium ions (Mg^{2+}) and sulfur ions (S^{2-}), with four oxygens thrown into the deal, too. The recipe is $MgSO_4$. Epsom salts were first discovered in Epsom, England, in the 1600s. However, it wasn't until the 1800s that magnesium was officially discovered as an element and given the name "magnesium."

Sir Humphry Davy was the scientist who discovered magnesium. He also discovered a number of other alkali elements including sodium, potassium, calcium, barium and strontium. He used electricity to pull alkali atoms away from their molecules. Davy used a simple battery (a Voltaic pile) to make positive and negative electrodes that could be put into chemical solutions containing alkali elements. The element ions would <u>go over</u> (remember, "ion" means "going") to one of the electrodes and stick there. In this way a whole clump of pure element could be produced. This is the way the alkali elements were isolated so they could be studied and named.

Davy was quite a showman, too. People would buy tickets to hear him lecture and to see him perform his chemistry demonstrations. One of his most famous demonstrations involved not alkali elements, but nitrogen and oxygen. When these two elements are joined to make N_2O, the result is a gas called nitrous oxide, or "laughing gas."

Alkali earth metals can be a lot of fun when they are added to explosives and shot up into the air. (Fireworks!) Magnesium burns white, calcium burns orange, strontium burns red, and barium burns green. Which one of these alkali earth metals is safe enough to use in sparklers? Is it on the top or bottom of the table? When the alkali metals burn in water, which one is the least dangerous? Where is it located on the table, top or bottom? Do you see a pattern?

The alkali metals also produce colors when they burn. Sodium, for example, burns with a yellow color. Sunlight is a yellow color because there is a lot of sodium in the sun. Sodium is also used in outdoor lighting. Sodium lights burn with an eerie yellow glow. Lithium burns pinkish-red and potassium burns lilac purple.

Activity 5.4 Watch some alkali elements go up in flames

Go to the YouTube playlist and look for the video(s) showing "flame tests." Each element burns with a different color. You can identify the elements in a compound by looking at the color of the flame.

A sample of barite in the form of a "desert rose."

Barium often bonds with sulfur to form **barium sulfate**, $BaSO_4$, also known as the mineral **barite**. (In the UK, it is spelled "baryte.") The Greek word "barus" means "heavy," and barium is, indeed, one of the heavier elements. The heaviness of barium is a great help to the oil and gas drilling industry. Barium powder is added to the drilling fluids in order to prevent blow-outs in wells. Barite is a natural, non-toxic substance, so it does not add any pollution to the environment.

Barium shows up very clearly on x-rays, so doctors will ask a patient to drink a liquid containing barium before the x-ray is taken. The barium makes every twist and turn of the digestive system visible.

When barium is combined with nitrogen and oxygen to make barium nitrate, you get a compound that burns bright green and is used in fireworks. Barium can be made toxic by combining it with carbon and oxygen to make barium carbonate. This compound has been used as rat poison.

Meanwhile, back in the laboratory of the Atomic Chef...

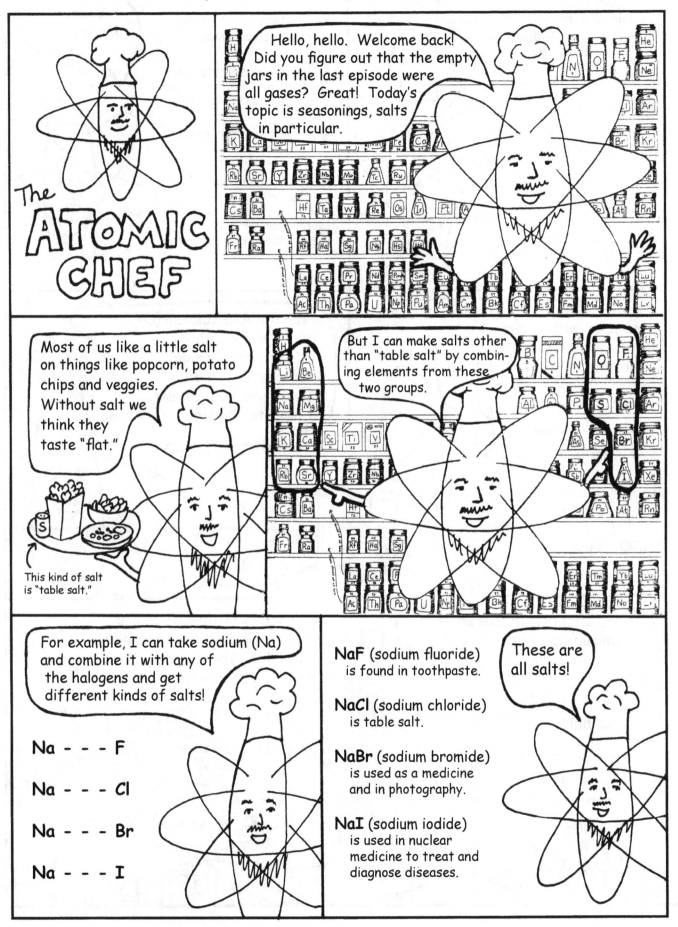

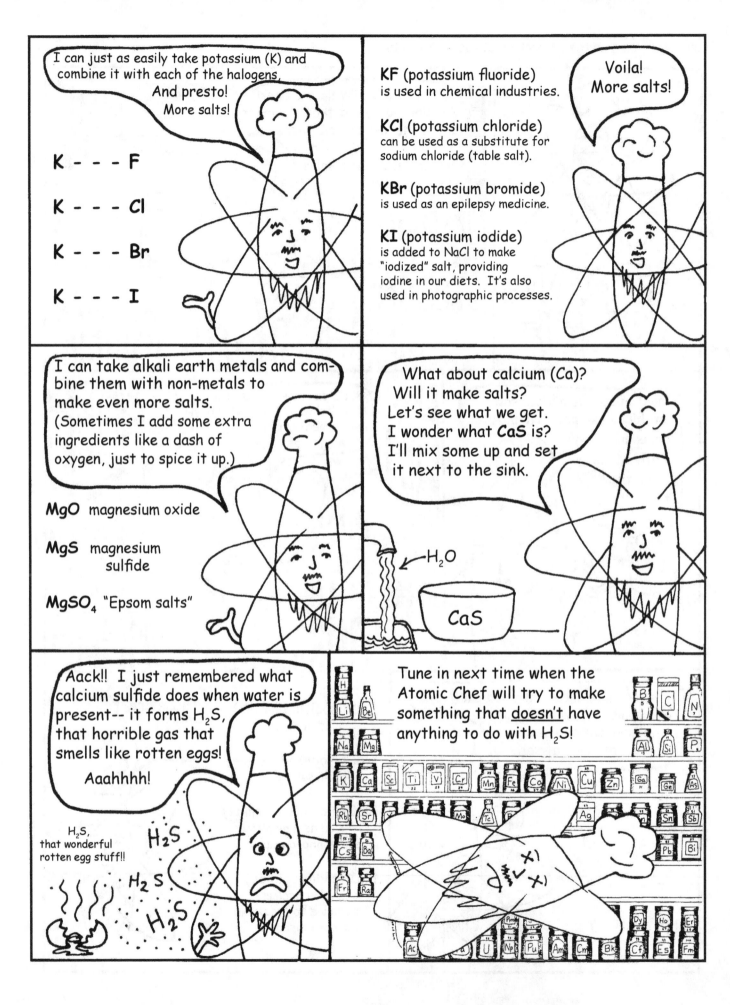

CHAPTER 6: THE NOBLE GASES AND THE NON-METALS

Think back to our Periodic Kingdom fairy tale. Do you remember the description of the Noble Gas family? They were the most peaceful rulers a kingdom could hope for. Nothing ever upset them. The real science behind this part of the story is that the noble gases are the only elements on the Table that have the exact number of electrons they want in their outer shells. Of course, using words like "peaceful" and "happy" to describe something that isn't alive is a little silly, but it does help us to remember the real science.

A chemist would say that the noble gases are "inert," which means they don't react with anything. An atom of helium doesn't want to give or get any electrons because its outer shell is full. Therefore, it will not interact with the atoms around it. Because it is inert, helium won't react with the atoms in your body, which is why it isn't dangerous to take a breath of it in order to talk funny.

Helium was named after the Greek god of the sun, "Helios," because the sun was the first place that helium was discovered. The discovery was made in the year 1868 using a machine called a **spectroscope**. If you look at a light source through a spectroscope you will see colored lines. Each element has a unique pattern of lines. Sodium's pattern is very simple and consists of basically two yellow lines. (To see the pattern you have to heat or burn the sodium so that it makes light.) Looking at the sun is a bit risky, as it can cause eye damage. The discoverers of helium looked at the sun during an eclipse, when the light was reduced and therefore less dangerous to look at. They saw sodium's

A scientist of the 1800s using a spectrometer

Helium's spectral pattern

two yellow lines, plus many others that they recognized, but they also saw a new pattern they didn't recognize. They understood that what they were seeing was probably a new element and they immediately named it helium, thinking it was a special element found only in the sun. Then, in 1903, large amounts of helium were found mixed in with natural gas deposits. Later, it was also found mixed in with uranium ore. Helium was definitely part of the earth's natural chemistry, not just the sun's. (Later, it was discovered that helium is a by-product of radioactive decay.)

Attribution: Atlant, on Wikipedia "xenon"

Because the noble gases are inert, they are ideal for use in light bulbs. They will not ignite or explode and are safe even when exposed to electrical currents. Neon is (obviously) used in neon lights, argon is used in ordinary bulbs, krypton is found in fluorescent bulbs and camera flashes, and xenon is put into ultraviolet lamps, camera flashes, and lighthouse bulbs. The xenon bulb shown here is used to project IMAX films, which require a very bright light source. Helium, neon and argon are also found in the most common types of lasers.

You may have heard that radon causes lung cancer. This noble gas is inert, just like all the others, so why does it cause problems? The problem with radon is not its electrons, but its nucleus. Radon is radioactive, which means its nucleus is throwing out harmful particles. Radon occurs naturally in the earth, especially in areas that have lots of uranium. Mostly, radon just goes up into the air and gets lost in the atmosphere. It only causes problems when a whole lot of it seeps up into the basement of a building or into a mine shaft.

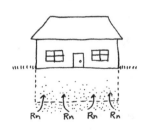

We already talked about one section of non-metals, the halogens. The other members of the non-metal group are carbon, nitrogen, oxygen, phosphorus, sulfur, and selenium. Some

chemists also include boron in the non-metal group. We could also include hydrogen as a non-metal if we wanted to. Hydrogen is sort of a group unto itself, but it is found connected to carbon and oxygen so often that we could legitimately think of it as a non-metal.

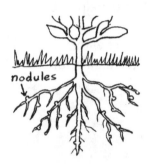

Nitrogen makes up almost 80% of the air we breathe. Nitrogen gas is made of two atoms of nitrogen bonded to each other to form N_2. The nitrogen we breathe doesn't do anything but take up space in our lungs. It's the oxygen that we need from the air. We do need nitrogen in our bodies, though, as it is an essential ingredient in proteins. The nitrogen atoms found in proteins come from the food we eat, however, not the air we breathe. Plants have a similar situation. They need nitrogen to make chlorophyll, but they can't get the nitrogen out of the air. Nitrogen is all around them, but the plants can't use it. For a plant to be able to take in nitrogen, the nitrogen atoms must be attached to molecules in the soil. Fortunately, there are bacteria in the soil that are capable of taking nitrogen out of the air and putting it into a form that plants can use. They are called "nitrogen-fixing" bacteria. You can find these bacteria growing in colonies on the roots of certain plants. The bacteria colony will look like a little bump about the size of the head of a pin. These bacteria prefer to grow on the roots of beans, peas, peanuts, soybeans and clover. Ancient farmers knew that these plants enriched the soil, but they did not know why. They rotated their crops each year, so that each field would get a turn having a bean crop in it. The beans would restore the nitrogen to the soil. In modern times, farmers just put nitrogen fertilizer on their fields.

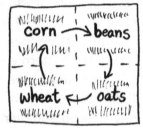

rotate each year

If you have a super-powerful refrigeration unit, and can cool nitrogen down to several hundred degrees below zero, it turns into a liquid—a very cold liquid, so cold that it can freeze things instantly. As soon as it is exposed to air or water, it boils and evaporates, returning to its gaseous state, returning to the air from whence it came.

Activity 6.1   Fun with liquid nitrogen

Liquid nitrogen isn't easy to get. It takes a special (expensive) refrigeration unit to get the temperature down to hundreds of degrees below zero. Fortunately, some folks who do have access to liquid nitrogen have filmed their demonstrations and posted them on the Internet. Go to YouTube.com/TheBasementWorkshop and you'll find some liquid nitrogen experiments on The Elements playlist.

Oxygen makes up about 20% of the air we breathe. Just like nitrogen, oxygen goes around in pairs (O_2). A single oxygen atom is a very unhappy atom because it has two empty electron slots in its outer shell. One oxygen atom by itself is very dangerous. We've learned to use this to our advantage, though, when we want to get rid of germs. Bleach, NaClO, has that single oxygen atom hanging on the end of the NaCl, and it can fall off very easily. When the oxygen atom falls off, it goes about looking for electrons. It will steal electrons from anything nearby, hopefully a germ that we want to kill anyway. A whole bunch of single oxygens can wreck a bacteria's molecules so badly that it dies.

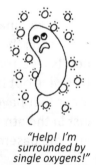

"Help! I'm surrounded by single oxygens!"

When two oxygen atoms pair up as O_2, the electron math doesn't work out perfectly. If each oxygen atom wants to get 2 electrons, then how can they be happy together? They work out an arrangement where they each share one of their electron pairs. Electrons move so fast that they can almost be in two places at the same time. Almost. So for a split second, one oxygen will have its own 6 electrons plus the 2 it is borrowing, to make 8 in the outer shell. For that split second it is happy. Then it must return the favor and share a pair with the other atom. This would mean that for a split second it would only have 4. But before it can get really unhappy about that, it's suddenly time to receive again, and it finds itself with 8 for another split second. This back and forth sharing happens so fast that the atoms feel like they have 8. Or at least they feel like they have 8 just often enough to prevent them from splitting up into singles. However, the fact that they are not completely content with the situation is also what makes them so useful to living things. They can be split up and used for many biological processes. Oxygen is also necessary for the energy-releasing process of combustion (burning).

Oxygen is a main ingredient in many minerals. Oxygen bonds with silicon to make silicon dioxide, SiO_2. Sand, glass and quartz crystals are made of SiO_2. The minerals hematite (Fe_2O_3) and magnetite (Fe_3O_4) are commonly found in the earth's crust. Even ice, which is frozen H_2O, can be classified as an oxide mineral.

A hematite carving

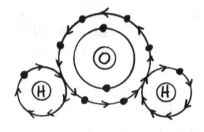

Speaking of H_2O, let's take a look at how these atoms stay together. We won't see an ionic bond here. Ionic bonds are formed only by the elements on the far sides of the table. An atom on the left side pairs up with an atom on the far right side, such as sodium and chlorine. Oxygen does not make ionic bonds. Non-metal atoms form a type of bond called covalent. In **covalent bonds**, electrons are actually shared, not given away. We won't see any electrically unbalanced atoms here. The atoms match themselves up so that they can all share their electrons. For example, oxygen has 6 electrons in its outer shell and hydrogen has 1. Two hydrogens can get together with one oxygen and all three of them together have a total of 8 electrons. The 8 electrons circulate around (at lightning speed) and make sure all the atoms are happy. (Of course, hydrogen is very small and doesn't want 8. It only wants 2.)

Another example of covalent bonding is carbon dioxide. One carbon atom gets together with two oxygen atoms. The oxygens would like to gain 2, and the carbon doesn't mind sharing its 4. As electrons move very quickly, the atoms can manage to share the 8's.

Sulfur also has 4 electrons in its outer shell. Sulfur can bond with two oxygens, just like carbon can. SO_2 is called sulfur dioxide. (You may be catching on by now that "di" means "two.") Sulfur dioxide

is a poisonous gas. When it is released into the air (often by coal-burning factories), it causes air pollution and acid rain. It's not just humans that make sulfur dioxide, though. Volcanoes make far more of it than any factory does.

Now here is a very strange covalent molecule: H_2O_2, hydrogen peroxide. This is the stuff that looks like water but is used for first aid, to clean cuts and scrapes on your skin. Let's do an electron count. The hydrogens each have 1 electron, and the oxygens each have 6. That's 6+6+1+1=14. Whoa! How can that be?

Hydrogen peroxide is water with an extra oxygen stuck on. Water is perfectly content the way it is. Why would it want another oxygen stuck onto it? This is another case of an oxygen atom that can easily fall off its molecule and become a dangerous single oxygen. If you want to kill germs, single oxygens can really help!

Phosphorus was first discovered in the year 1669 when a chemist was boiling a batch of... urine. No kidding, he collected hundreds of gallons of pee and was going to boil it until it turned into gold. (Well, urine is yellow, gold is yellow—could be a connection there.) What his experiment produced was far more amazing than gold. It looked like a disgusting lump of yuck (and it smelled terrible) but when he heated it, it glowed with a brilliant white light. Back in the 1600s they had never seen a light bulb, so glowing phosphorus must have seemed almost magical. He had discovered one of phophorus' more interesting qualities. The name phosphorus means "light-bearer."

Pure phosphorus can be either white or red. In white phosphorus you find 4 atoms binding together to cope with their three empty electron slots. Eventually, white phosphorus turns into red phosphorus as those foursomes split apart. You've seen red phosphorus on the tips of matches. Match heads also contain sulfur, another non-metal.

Phosphorus is also involved in energetic tasks in living cells. When combined with oxygen, it's the P in the ATP—a molecule that acts like a rechargeable battery. Phosphorus is necessary in other process, also. Many foods contain phosphorus, so most of us receive plenty in our diet. Carbonated beverages often acid phosphoric acid to give the refreshing sour snap, though the sour must be balanced by lots of sugar. Because of all the sugar, carbonated beverages do more harm than good.

White phosphorus

Carbon is the most amazing atom in the non-metal group. Because it has a valence of +4 or -4, it can bond with itself or with other atoms in all kinds of ways. When carbon bonds with itself, it can make something as humble and inexpensive as graphite (the "lead" in pencils) or as valuable as a diamond. It may be hard to believe, but graphite and diamonds both have the same chemical recipe: just carbon. How, then, can they be so different?

To discover the answer we must look at how the carbons are bonded to each other. In the case of diamond, the basic geometrical shape looks like a pyramid. When millions upon millions of these molecules are bonded together like this, we get a diamond. The bonds in this shape are very strong, which is what makes diamonds so hard.

Another shape that carbon can bond into is a six-sided hexagon. Graphite is layer upon layer of flat sheets of connected hexagons. The sheets are only loosely held together, and can slide back and forth. This is why pencils rub off onto paper, and why graphite can be used as a dry lubricant. (Graphite from a pencil can be rubbed onto the bottom of wooden dresser drawers to make them slide in and out more easily.) Technically, if you could squeeze the graphite in your pencil hard enough to make the carbons change their geometry from hexagons into pyramids, you could make a diamond.

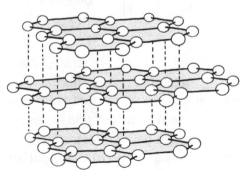

The most fantastic shape carbon can make looks exactly like a soccer ball. Sixty carbons join together to form a sphere made of hexagons and pentagons. Since this shape looks a bit like the geodesic domes used in architecture, it was named after an architect famous for designing geodesic domes, Buckminster Fuller. Chemists decided to name this molecule "buckminsterfullerene," (or "buckyball" for short).

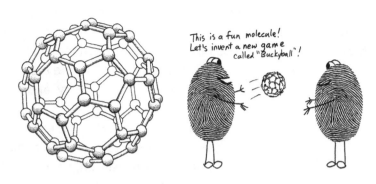

Carbon is the central atom in all organic molecules. We call molecules "organic" if they are organized around carbon atoms. Some types of organic molecules are found in plants, animals and microorganisms, such as DNA, proteins, sugars and starches. You are have undoubtedly seen drawings of the DNA molecule, with its intriguing and beautiful double helix shape. You are very familiar the organic molecules called proteins, starches, and fats because you eat them every day. You need to eat them because they are the raw materials your body uses to make its cells and organs. You are made of thousands of different types of carbon-based molecules.

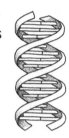

Other kinds of organic molecules aren't found in living things. The molecules that plastic is made of, for example, are called organic because they contain long chains of carbon atoms. Gasoline and other petroleum products are made of long strings of carbon atoms and are therefore classified as organic.

Pure sulfur is a yellow solid.

Garlic gets it smell from the sulfur compounds it contains.

Sulfur is right under oxygen on the Periodic Table. This means it also has 6 electrons in its outer shell, and would like to gain 2 more to make 8. It will, therefore, have some chemical similarities to oxygen. However, sulfur atoms are larger than oxygen atoms, having an atomic mass (weight) double that of oxygen. Larger atoms are less likely to be gases. (Krypton, xenon and radon are curious exceptions to this rule.) Pure sulfur is found as a yellow solid and has a strong odor. That's one of sulfur's characteristics—it smells. Sulfur is found in many organic molecules in both plants and animals. It's the key element in the stink of skunks and garlic. When eggs go rotten, they produce hydrogen sulfide, H_2S, which smells bad in a sulfur-ish way.

Sulfur is part of several amino acids (the stuff that proteins are made of). Its presence in hair proteins makes hair waterproof. Sulfur can allow molecules to make "cross-bridges" which makes them tougher. It can be added to rubber to keep it from melting in high temperatures and cracking in low temperatures.

Selenium is right under sulfur in the Periodic Table, which means it has the same number of electrons in its outer shell. Since selenium has the same valency as sulfur, it is sometimes found in minerals that usually contain sulfur, with selenium taking the place of sulfur. The metal atoms in these minerals are happy with either sulfur or selenium; it doesn't make a significant difference to them. Both S and Se want to make 2 bonds, and that's the most important issue to the metal atoms. They'll bond with either one.

Selenium's name comes from the Greek word for the moon, "selene." Selenium doesn't have any features of the moon. It seems that the discoverer of selenium noticed its striking similarities to the element tellurium, right underneath it on the Table. He thought that since tellurium was named after the earth, perhaps the "earth element" should have a "moon element" above it. Or so the story goes.

Selenium is named after the moon.

Selenium is found in some key molecules in our bodies, but it is not as abundant as oxygen and sulfur. Some people take selenium supplements because selenium is needed to build protective enzymes that can catch dangerous fragments of broken molecules, called "free radicals."

Selenium used to be used quite a bit in the electronics industry, but now silicon has taken over. Selenium is still used by the glass making industry, and it is also a key ingredient in solar cells.

The halogens (fluorine, chlorine, bromine, iodine and astatine) are a subset of the non-metal group. We can think of them as non-metals, or as the salt-making halogens. Both are correct.

Some chemists like to put boron, silicon, arsenic and tellurium into the non-metal group, as well. This causes a lot of confusion for chemistry students. If you do a search on the Internet for Periodic Tables, you will find that some tables color code these elements to be in the non-metal group. Other tables will have them color coded to match the metal group along with aluminum and tin. And still others will split the difference and put them into their own group called the semi-metals. Who should we believe? In the end, it doesn't matter too much how they are classified because the elements don't care, and classification doesn't change them in any way. They are what they are, no matter what we call them. Perhaps the most important lesson to learn here is that scientists don't always agree!

Activity 6.2   Watch a demonstration that uses noble gases

Except for helium, noble gases are not items we can buy at a store. Therefore, we have to rely on generous scientists who take the time to post their noble gas video demonstrations. There should be one or more posted for you at the Elements playlist. One of them shows six balloons, each one filled with a different noble gas. What will happen when the demonstrator lets them go? Helium is easy to predict, but what about xenon?

If you like silly animated cartoons, you'll like the video with funny rhymes and cartoon pictures about the noble gases.

Activity 6.3   A famous silly song about the elements

A number of years ago, an entertainer named Tom Lehrer wrote and performed "The Elements Song." The lyrics of the song are simply the names of the elements, rearranged so that they rhyme. (This means they are not in order, so you can't use this song to memorize the Table.)   There are several versions of this song posted on The Elements playlist on the YouTube channel. One version is a historical film (in black and white) of Mr. Lehrer performing his song for an audience. Another version provides a nice picture of each element as it is named, and a third version has the song slowed down so you have a better chance of being able to sing along.

Activity 6.4   A puzzle about carbon-based molecules

There's nothing like carbon when you want to form bonds. Carbon bonds in more ways and with more elements than anything else on the Periodic Table. It's the "nice guy" among the elements. You could imagine it being willing to shake hands and form friendships with just about anyone. It also likes to link up with other carbons and make long chains. Long chains of carbon atoms that have hydrogens all along the sides are called **hydrocarbons**. Small hydrocarbon chains make things like natural gas (methane) and gasoline (petroleum). Medium-sized chains make things like wax, paraffin, and tar. Really long chains are found in plastics. Hydrocarbon chains can have other atoms attached to them, too, besides hydrogens. When chlorine joins the chain, we get PVC plastic (polyvinyl chloride) that is used for plumbing pipes.

Carbon also forms the "backbone" of many of the molecules in your body. Carbon atoms are the foundation, or anchoring points, for the other atoms in the molecules. Attached to the carbons, you'll find many of our non-metal friends: hydrogen, oxygen, nitrogen, phosphorus, and sulfur. In specialized bio molecules, you might find some metal atoms such as iron (in hemoglobin that carries oxygen) or zinc (in molecules that control DNA). Carbon and its non-metal friends can be combined in almost endless ways, forming the vast number of biological molecules that make living things.

In this puzzle, write the letter symbol that goes with the atomic number written under each blank. For example, for the number 6 you would write the letter "C" for carbon. The letters will spell out the name of a substance that has carbon-based molecules. (Some letters don't appear by themselves on the table, so they have been written in.)

1) __ __ __ __ __
   15 57 16 22 6

2) __ __ __ __ __
   31 16 8 3 10

3) __ __ __ __
   59 8 91 10

4) __ __ __ __ T
   33 15 1 13

5) __ __ __ L
   13 27 67

6) __ __ __ __ __
   5 92 6 19 39

7) __ __ __ E __ __
   20 9 9 53 10

8) __ __ __   __ __ D
   95 49 8   89 53
   (building block of proteins)

9) __ __ __
   9 85 16
   (a type of wax)

10) __ __ __ __ __
    91 88 9 9 49

Carbon holding 4 H's

11) __ L __ __ __ R
    84 39 99 52

12) G __ __ __
    71 27 34
    (a sugar)

__ __ L
5 13

Carbon is always drawn in black.

13) __ __
    105 77

Carbon can hold hands in 4 places!

14) G __ __ __
    71 52 7

15) __ __ L __ __
    7 39 8 7

16) __ __ __ __ __ __ __
    18 22 9 53 6 53 13

__ __ __ __ RS
9 57 23 8

17) __ __ __ T __ __ __ R
    15 57 7 9 53 4

TRIVA QUIZ: What two letters of the alphabet do not appear in any of the symbols on the Periodic Table?

Activity 6.5   Practice makes perfect!

Here is a review activity to jog your memory about what you learned in past chapters.

1) If an atom could be enlarged to be the size of a sports stadium and the nucleus was sitting in the middle of the field, about how big would the nucleus be?
a) the size of a watermelon   b) the size of a marble   c) the size of a car   d) the size of an elephant

2) What do you call an atom that has more electrons than protons, or more protons than electrons?
a) an alkali   b) an isotope   c) radioactive   d) an ion   e) covalent

3) What is the valence number for oxygen? a) -2   b) -1   c) 0   d) +1   e) +2

4) What "family group" on the Periodic Table is perfectly happy? _____

5) What "family group" has only 1 electron in their outer shells? _____

6) What "family group" has 7 electrons in their outer shells? _____

7) Which element causes the stink in skunks and garlic? _____

8) Which element can form a circle called a buckyball? _____

9) Which element is taken from the air by bacteria and put into the soil? _____

10) Which element was first discovered in the sun? _____

Match the formulas with their common names. (Word bank: plaster, sand, Teflon, salt, bleach)
11) SiO_2 _____
12) NaCl _____
13) NaClO _____
14) C_2F_4 _____
15) $CaSO_4$ _____

"We know all the answers but we're not not telling!"

16) An atom of magnesium is most likely to bond with: a) N   b) C   c) O   d) F   e) Ne

17) An atom of potassium is most likely to bond with: a) Na   b) B   c) Ca   d) Mg   e) Cl

18) The atomic number is the number of _____ that an atom has.

19) Which of these things is NOT made of carbon?   a) diamonds   b) graphite   c) coal   d) glass

20) Which of these statements is NOT true about electrons?
a) Electrons don't like to be close to each other.   b) Electrons like to "work" in pairs.
c) Electrons have a positive electrical charge.   d) Electrons weigh almost nothing.

BONUS QUESTIONS (a little harder)

1) What atom is this? $1s^2 2s^2 2p^6 3s^2 3p^4$? _____

2) Protons and neutrons have a mass (weight) of 1 amu (atomic mass unit). The mass of an atom is equal to the number of protons plus the number of neutrons. If an atom of uranium has a mass of 238 and uranium's atomic number is 92, then how many neutrons does this atom have? _____

3) When you see a number outside of the parentheses, like the 2 in this formula: $(OH)_2$, that means you have two of whatever is inside of those parentheses, in this case 2 (OH)'s. So you have 2 O's and 2 H's.

How many O's (oxygens) are in this mineral? _____ $Ca_{10}Mg_2Al_4(SiO_4)_5(Si_2O_7)_2(OH)_4$

CHAPTER 7: METALS: SEMI-, PURE, AND TRANSITION

Working our way to the south and the west in our Periodic Kingdom, we come to the semi-metals. They live along the diagonal line, in between the metals and the non-metals. In our fairy tale, we made up that part about the non-metal family having a difficult last name that no one could remember. It just sounded like a logical reason for them to be called non-metals, and it made the story more interesting. But it is true that the semi-metals can also be called the metalloids. You will see both names used equally.

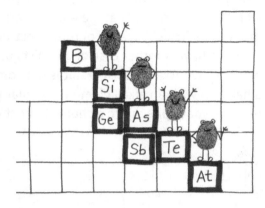

The metalloid neighborhood is anything but a settled place. Chemists don't all agree about exactly where the dividing line is. Some say boron should be a metalloid, others say not. Some say polonium should be a metalloid, others say it is a true metal. So don't be overly concerned about trying to remember which are which because chemists don't even know for sure! In this booklet, we'll just choose the pattern that is easiest to remember. We are going to use a stair-step right down the diagonal, then add two squares under the middle. Looks nice, eh?

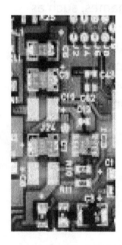

The only metalloid we'll discuss is silicon. (The others are used in high-tech industries in various ways, and astatine is radioactive—more about that in the next chapter.) Have you ever heard of "Silicon Valley" in California? You might think that's where you can find a lot of silicon in the soil, but the name actually comes from the industry that goes on there: computers and microchips. Because silicon is on the borderline between metals and non-metals, it can act like both. Sometimes it can act like a metal and be very good at carrying electricity, but in other situations it acts like a non-metal and is an insulator that doesn't carry electricity. Silicon is the ideal element for making some of the electronic parts that are used in computers and other high-tech equipment. Silicon Valley is an area that has a large number of high-tech computer companies. The element silicon has come to represent all computer-based technology.

Silicon is also one of the most abundant elements on the planet. It is one of the main ingredients in many kinds of rocks. Volcanic lava is high in silicon, so when it cools, the rocks it forms are high in silicon. We've already seen that the chemical recipe for sand is SiO_2. Strangely enough, when small amounts of other elements are mixed in with SiO_2, it isn't ruined. The impurities turn it into a variety of semi-precious gemstones, such as jasper, agate, opal, amethyst, onyx, and chalcedony. The purple mineral shown here is amethyst and below it is an agate.

In the world of biology, silicon is used by some animals, such as diatoms, to make their hard outer shells. Others, like sea sponges, use silicon for their structural skeletons. (Most shelled animals use calcium instead of silicon.)

a diatom

purple amethyst and striped agate

59

The true metals have only three members that most people have heard of: aluminum, tin and lead. The others, gallium, indium, thallium, bismuth, and polonium, are not well-known. (You've probably heard of bismuth without being aware of it. The "bis" in "PeptoBismol" stands for bismuth. Bismuth is one of the key ingredients!) Before you started reading this book, if we had asked you to name some true metals, you would probably have included elements such as copper, nickel, iron, silver and gold. It's surprising that these elements we know as metals are not in the true metal family on the Periodic Table. When chemists named the groups, they were looking primarily at the electron arrangements, not at how the elements are used. The "true" metals are "true" because of their electron configurations and, therefore, their location on the Table. Here we have another case of chemists using common words in a different way. We saw this with the word "salt." To a chemist, a salt is not something you put on food. It's what you get when you combine a halogen with an alkali element. Similarly, chemists use the word metal in a way that is different from our everyday speech. To a chemist, most of the elements on the Periodic Table are metals.

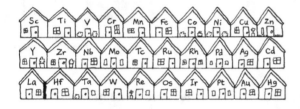

Next we come to the very large neighborhood right in the middle of the table, where all the transition metals live. In our story, they were the hard-working people of the kingdom who worked at industrial jobs. Many of the elements in this block have familiar names, such as titanium, chromium, iron, cobalt, nickel, copper, zinc, silver, cadmium, tungsten, platinum, gold, and mercury. Others are strangers to you, such as yttrium, niobium, molybdenum, osmium and iridium. You might look at some of their names and be afraid to pronounce them. One way to become comfortable with things that seem hard is to introduce them in ways that seem amusing. So here's a funny introduction to five of these strange transition metals.

The strangest neighbor on the block is technetium *(tek-NEE-shee-um)*. His next-door neighbors report that they've seen harmful radioactivity coming out of his house. And most of the time he isn't even home. Everyone says he doesn't belong in this neighborhood because no one else is radioactive, but when he shows them his electron configuration, he does indeed fit right between molybdenum *(moll-LIB-den-um)* and

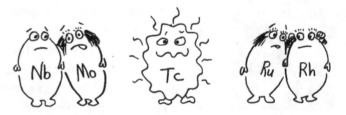

Molly leans over to gossip with Mr. Niobium, and Ruth whispers to her friend, Rhoda.

ruthenium. Poor Molly and Ruth! Ruth spends a lot of time gossiping to her neighbor, Rhoda, about it. Before technetium moved in, he lived at the nuclear power plant. He said that's where he was born. Fortunately for the neighbors, he's not around most of the time.

Technitium's stable neighbors, niobium, molybdenum, ruthenium and rhodium are often combined with other metals in order to improve their chemistry for making things like tools, heaters, bulbs, lasers, and spark plugs. Unlike its neighbors, technetium is a synthetic (man-made) element and is often a by-product of nuclear fission in a nuclear power plant. Since it is man-made, the number of neutrons in its nucleus can be controlled to some degree. Technetium atoms with 56 neutrons are less dangerous and their radioactivity wears off in about 6 hours. This makes them suitable for use in medical applications such as doing scans to determine areas of disease. (Molly won't want to admit this, but sometimes atoms of molybdenum are used to make this type of technetium. How can this be? Remember, it's the number of protons that defines an element. Add a proton to Mo, and you get Tc.)

There are so many transition metals that we can't discuss each one. Fortunately, you are probably already at least somewhat familiar with many of them, such as gold, silver, iron, copper, nickel, zinc, platinum and mercury. Others, such as tungsten, might have unfamiliar names, but we interact with them all the time without even knowing it. Tungsten is what those thin filaments inside light bulbs are made of. Cadmium is used in rechargeable batteries, and we see chromium on the surfaces of shiny tools and car parts. Vanadium is an ingredient in the metals that are used to make wrenches and pliers.

When two or more metals are mixed together we call this mixture an **alloy**. One of the first alloys ever discovered was **bronze**. Ancient metal workers found that when they added some tin to their molten copper, the result was a metal that was much better than just plain copper. Bronze was harder and more durable than copper, making it better for weapons and statues. Later, during the Roman period, zinc was added to copper to make **brass**. Brass was even more durable than bronze, and if you added some aluminum or iron to the mix, the resulting metal was very resistant to corrosion and could be used to make parts for boats that were constantly exposed to salty ocean water. Metal workers over the centuries tried adding tiny amounts of various other elements, such as arsenic, phosphorus or manganese. Each element would have an effect on the final product, letting them adjust the quality of the metal to suit the application it was being used for. One of the brass alloys is ideal for making musical instruments such as trumpets and trombones. Another variation of brass is used to make cymbals.

a bronze statue

A volatic pile similar to the ones that Humphry Davy used to discover sodium.
(Image: Wikipedia, GuidoB.)

Metals have another important characteristic, besides being durable—they can carry an electrical current. Some metals are better than others at conducting electricity, but all metals are at least somewhat conductive. The very best conductors are silver, copper and gold. Since copper is much less expensive than silver and gold, it is the best choice for electrical wires. Nickel, zinc, iron, cobalt and tin are in the middle, and lead is at the bottom of the list. (The transition metals we have not mentioned are somewhere in the middle, too, but listing all of them is a bit much. If you want to see a list, you can always consult the Internet.)

An Italian scientist named Alessandro Volta figured out how to use copper and zinc to produce electricity. He made a stack of three types of discs: copper, zinc and leather saturated with salt water. The salt water discs between the copper and zinc allowed the electrical current to flow to the next set of discs. Voltaic piles were fairly easy to make, and soon many scientists were making them. One of those scientists was Humphry Davy, who used as many as 100 piles hooked together to make a dangerously strong current. Davy's electricity was strong enough to isolate pure sodium atoms. But how did these piles work? What was happening inside the metals? It wouldn't be until the 20th century that the answer was discovered.

A copper wire is made of millions of copper atoms stuck together, so obviously copper atoms stick to other copper atoms. They don't use ionic or covalent bonding, though. The transition metals use their own type of bonding called **metallic bonding**. When these elements get together, they don't keep track of their own personal electrons very well. Their electrons are free to wander about. It's sort of like a parent saying to a child, "You can play anywhere in the neighborhood, just don't leave

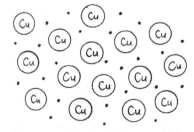
Copper's outer shell electrons are free to move about.

the neighborhood." The child might go next door to play in his neighbor's yard, or he might wander down the street a bit. However, in the atomic world (unlike the real world) you can't rule out the possibility that the electron "child" might actually wander off permanently. Electrons are not individuals like humans are. All electrons are the same. If a copper atom's outer electron wandered off and another one came to take its place, the copper atom would never know the difference. Will the copper's electron stay in the area? Probably. Will it leave? Maybe.

While it is true that electricity is made of moving electrons, we shouldn't think of a stream of electricity as being like a stream of water. Rather, a better analogy might be a row of dominoes. In a domino rally, the dominoes move and we see a pattern of motion being carried along from one end to the other, but the dominoes basically stay in the same place. Or, you could think of a row of people standing in a line. The first one in the line pushes the second one, who pushes the third one, and so on down the line. (The people would not have to be reset like the domino rally would, so perhaps the people are a slightly better analogy.)

Look at the Periodic Table and you will see that copper, silver and gold are all in the same column, with copper on top, silver in the middle and gold on the bottom. Remember, the columns tell us about the arrangement of the electrons in the outer shell. For example, all the elements in the noble gas column have full outer shells and all the halogens have one less than they'd like. The Quick-And-Easy Atomizer activity showed us that the placement of electrons up to argon is fairly straightforward. If we had kept going, however, it would have gotten messy. With the transition metals, things are

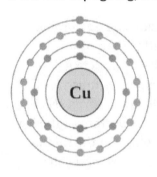

An over-simplified drawing of copper's electrons. The s, p and d orbitals are not shown.

not so straightforward. The addition of the 10-seater "d" shell makes things more complicated. Every time an electron is added, the "math" changes. Transition metals can decide how to split up the electrons into the s, p and d orbitals in a way that maximizes electron "happiness" (or at least minimizes "unhappiness"). The diagram shown here is the one you will see if you search the Internet for "copper electrons." It shows you the end result of what copper has done with its electrons, but it does not show you the s, p and d orbitals. That one outer electron is actually sitting in the 2-seater s orbital, which should have been filled first, according to our Atomizer rules. Copper decided that it was better to have a half-filled 2-seater orbital than to have a 10-seater orbital with one electron missing. Copper likes the fraction "1/2" better than "9/10."

Having just one electron in the outer shell doesn't make these elements act like an alkali metal, though. Copper, silver and gold certainly don't explode when you put them in water! Quite the opposite—they are very stable. In the transition neighborhood, having one outer electron makes you very good at conducting electricity.

One last characteristic of transition metals really needs to be mentioned. If you start peeking into higher level chemistry books, it won't take you long to discover that many of these elements have multiple valencies (which are usually called "oxidation states"). Chromium, for example, has three options: (+2), (+3) and (+6). Chromium's oxidation number (valency) depends on what atom, or atoms, it is bonding with. It's the same with copper and iron and many other metals. Their oxidation states can change so that they can bond with atoms such as oxygen, nitrogen, chlorine, or carbon. This makes learning chemistry a lot more difficult, but it also allows for a larger variety of minerals to exist. Our world is more beautiful, more diverse and more interesting because transition metals have more than one oxidation state (valency).

A colorful opal from Wikipedia (Dpulitzer)

Activity 7.1   "The Bonding Song"

Now that you know about all three types of bonding, you are ready for "The Bonding Song." There are two audio tracks, one with the words and one without, so that after learning how the words go, you can sing it yourself. (If you don't already have the audio tracks, you can access them by going to: www.ellenjmchenry.com/audio-tracks-for-the-elements)   The tune might sound familiar, as it was borrowed from the American folk song, "Turkey in the Straw."

The Bonding Song

There were two little atoms and they both were very sad,
They wanted eight e's but six was all they had,
Then they hit upon a plan and decided they would share:
They each gave the other an electron pair.
Covalent bond – sharing is great!
Covalent bond – now they both have eight!
Outer shells want eight electrons,
So non-metal atoms form covalent bonds.

There were two little atoms, they were sad as you might guess,
They wanted eight e's, one had more and one had less,
Then they hit upon a plan and one atom said,
"I'll give my extra e's if you agree to wed."
Ionic bond – one atom gives!
Ionic bond – one atom gets!
Atoms give and take their electrons
And they stay right close together with an ionic bond.

There were lots of little atoms, they were metals every one,
They were all in a clump, they were having lots of fun,
And the way they stuck together was to share their e's around;
They called their little clump a metallic bond.
Metallic bond – everyone gives!
Metallic bond – everyone gets!
Electrons float and belong to everyone,
And the metals stick together with metallic bonds.

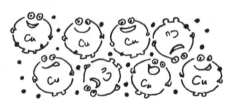

Activity 7.2   An online quiz about metals

Here's a just-for-fun quiz game you can do to test your knowledge of metals. If you don't know the answers, just guess—you'll still learn! (This link has been stable over the years, but if you find that it doesn't work, try searching the Internet with key words "online quiz metals.")

http://www.syvum.com/cgi/online/serve.cgi/squizzes/chem/metals.tdf?0

Activity 7.3   Finish memorizing the Table up to radon

Why in the world would you want to do this? Well... if you are going into chemistry some day, the answer is obvious. If not, it's still kind of a cool thing to do and a great way to impress your relatives at holiday gatherings. If nothing else, it's good exercise for your brain, like lifting weights is good for your muscles. However, it is also optional. If you've had enough memorizing, that's okay.

If you want to try it but feel like you need some help, you might want to use a "mnemonic" (the first "m" is silent). A mnemonic is a story, a picture, or even a silly idea, that helps you to remember something. It's not cheating, it's just being clever about helping your brain to make information stick better. Here is a mnemonic story about the next two lines on the table, in case you find it helpful, (and yes, it is very silly), but you could also make up your own.

RUBy was the STRongest woman in her town. Y, her muscle "Z-R" the "N-B"
rubidium   strontium   yttrium   zirconium   niobium
"Why"   "they are"   "envy"

of everyone. Her friend, MOLLY, claims Ruby won the river race fair and square.
                    molybdenum

TECHnically, RUTH, RHOD faster, but she was a PAL and AG-cepted the silver
technetium   ruthenium rhodium   palladium
"rowed"

medal instead. Before the race, a CAD named INDY, took a pair of tin SNips,
                              cadmium   indium

ANT SaBotaged her boat. She yelled at him, "I can TELLUR a cheater!"
antimony = Sb   tellurium
"and"   "tell you're"

She punched him and they had to put IODINE on the cut.   Queen XENON

sent Indy to the dungeon.

Once there were two brothers, CESIUM and BARIIUM. Their science homework

was to research LANTHANUM and the LANTHANIDE series. Cesium said,

"We'll HAF-TA check out the WWW. You can REally get a lot of information there."
       hafnium tantalum   tungsten = W   rhenium
       "have to"   "World Wide Web"

Just then, their dog, OSMIUM, came in. "IRrr," he growled. He had an empty
                                          iridium

PLATe in his mouth. "A-U HoG!" shouted Cesium. "You can TL he ate our PB
platinum   Au = gold Hg = mercury   Tl = thallium   Pb = lead
"Hey, you hog!"   "tell"   "peanut butter"

sandwiches!" Barium said,"That's okay, we can always BI more. Or we can eat
                                                    Bi = bismuth
                                                    "buy"

POLOgna istead." AT last, we've made it to RADON!
Polonium   At = astatine
"bologna"

Activity 7.4   Who am I?   (A guessing game about <u>pure metals</u> and <u>semi-metals</u>)

1) _____ I have a very low melting point. This means I might even melt in your hand. I was named using the old Latin word for France.

2) _____ Although I am famous for being poisonous and was once used in pesticides, many living things (including humans) need me in very small amounts. When combined with gallium I am an important ingredient in electronic devices.

3) _____ My letter symbol does not match my name. Many years ago, I was used for water pipes, but not any more because I am fairly toxic. I am very dense, which makes me feel heavy.

4) _____ I used to be called stibium. In the ancient world, I was used in cosmetics. Now I am mainly used in fire-proofing and in lead-acid batteries.

5) _____ My name means "indigo blue" because I have a bright blue line in my spectrum when I am burned. I am similar to my Periodic neighbors and have a low melting point, making me useful for soldering. I am also used in high-tech products such as semiconductors.

6) _____ I am best known for my alloys. If you add me to copper, you get bronze. I used to be made into cans, but now they use aluminum instead.

7) _____ I sit right next to a liquid element, but I am not a liquid. My name means "bright green twig" because I have a bright green line in my spectrum. I am used in high-tech industry as an ingredient in sensors and detectors, but don't eat me because I am poisonous.

8) _____ I sit next to many toxic metals, but I am not poisonous. In fact, I am used in medicines and cosmetics. I was often confused with antimony since we have many similarities due to the fact that we are in the same column on the Periodic Table.

9) _____ My name comes from the Latin word for "earth." I am very rare so I am used in small quantities. I am added to copper and lead to make alloys that are more easily "machined" than they would be otherwise. I have some chemical similarities to selenium and sulfur.

10) _____ I am the third most abundant element in the earth's crust. I am one of the least dense elements, making me feel very light. I am not magnetic at all, but I do conduct electricity.

11) _____ My atoms are very small. I am found in some laundry powders and I am used to make fiberglass insulation. One of my acid compounds is used as an antiseptic eyewash.

12) _____ I am very important to the electonics industry because I can be either an electrical conductor or an insulator, depending on circumstances. I am also very abundant in the crust of the earth. You walked on me when you went to the beach.

Activity 7.5   Research your favorite transition metal

Choose a transition metals that you'd like to know more about. Use the following page to record the findings of your research. If you'd like to research more than one transition element, you can make an extra copy (or copies) of the page before you write on it.

symbol

name of element

atomic mass

number of protons

number of neutrons

number of electrons

atomic number

At standard temperature and pressure (STP), this element is a:

☐ solid
☐ liquid
☐ gas

Where did this element get its name?

At what temperature will this element boil?

At what temperature will this element melt or freeze?

What group does this element belong to?

☐ alkali metals
☐ alkali earth metals
☐ transition metals
☐ true metals
☐ semi-metals (metalloids)
☐ non-metals

Is this element found in the Earth's crust? ☐ yes ☐ no If so, where?

☐ rocks ☐ dirt   ☐ lava
☐ water ☐ gemstones
☐ sand   ☐ _____

When was this element first discovered?

Who discovered it?

Is this element ever found all by itself (not part of a compound)? ☐ yes ☐ no

What color is this element? (Or, if it is never found by itself, what color is its most common compound?)

Other colors?

Is this element used in industry? ☐ yes ☐ no If so, what is it used for?

Is this element found in the human body? ☐ yes ☐ no
Is it part of the structure of the body? ☐ yes ☐ no
Can this element be harmful to the body? ☐ yes ☐ no
If it is harmful, how might you ingest it or come into contact with it?

Is this element used in any art or craft? ☐ yes ☐ no
What type of art uses it?
☐ painting   ☐ sculpture   ☐ pottery
☐ printing   ☐ coins   ☐ jewelry
☐ _____

Is this element used in medicine or dentistry? ☐ yes ☐ no
If so, how is it used?

Give one historical fact about this element other than the date of its discovery:

Draw a picture of a molecule containing this element:

What do you think is the most interesting fact about this element?

Name of molecule:

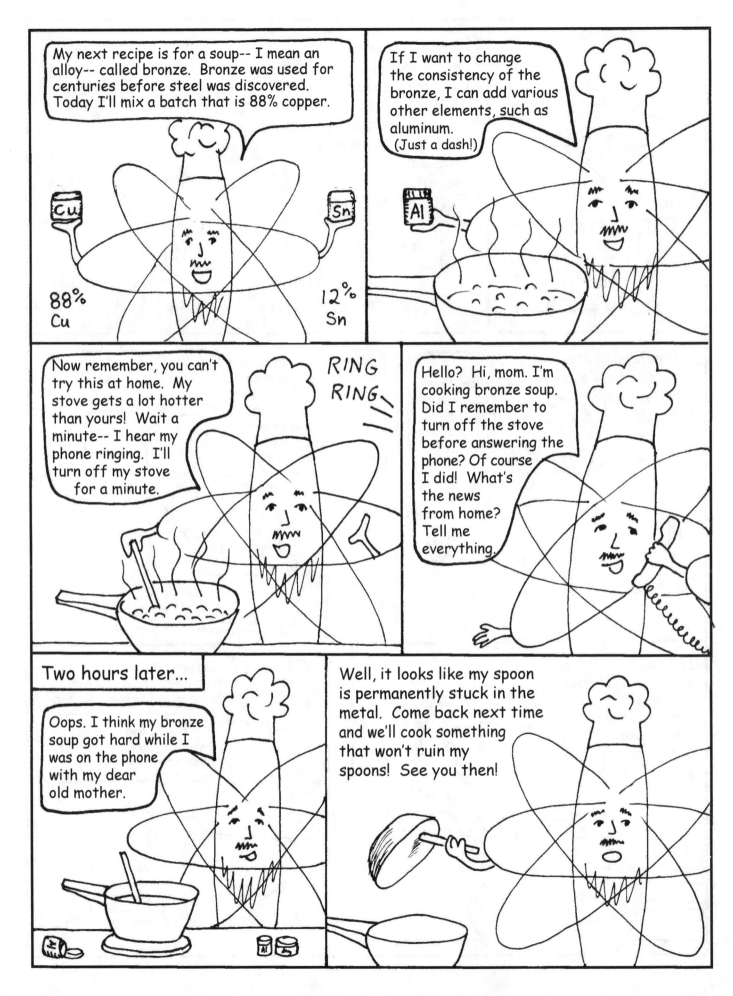

CHAPTER 8: THE LANTHANIDES AND ACTINIDES

The lanthanide and actinide series are almost always shown as two separate rows, sitting below the main table, as if they were not really part of the table. Actually, they <u>are</u> part of the table, and if we put them in where they belong, the table would look like this:

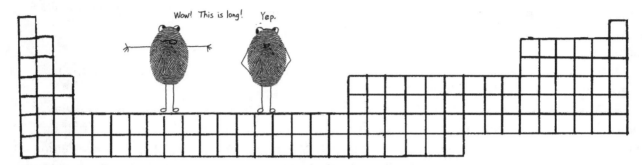

The problem with this table is just practical—it doesn't fit very well on a single page. By the time you shrink it down enough to get it onto the page, the squares are so small that you can't read the information written in the boxes. It's so long that it's awkward. Taking out the longest, skinniest part, the lanthanide and actinide rows, makes the table look much better. The crack in the street in the Periodic Kingdom is where these two rows should go.

What are these two rows? In the Periodic Kingdom the lanthanides were industrious miners who provided rare metals for high-tech products. The real science is very close to this picture!

These elements were once thought to be very rare, although we now know they are more abundant in the Earth's crust than silver or gold. We can still call them rare, though, because you don't find them sitting around in their pure form waiting to be collected. No one has ever gone panning for neodymium like they would for gold. You don't find chunks of solid cerium when digging with a shovel, as you might with copper. These rare earth metals are more difficult to get out of the rocks in which they are found because they are mixed in with so many other things.

A rock that contains minerals is called an "ore." This picture shows an ore that contains rare earths. The penny sitting on it lets you know how big the rock is. Miners dig up the ore, then have to figure out how to get the elements out of the ore. This usually involves crushing and heating the rocks, plus the addition of chemicals. Only after a lot of work is the pure element obtained. The rare earths present a problem for the refiners because the temperature at which they melt is very high. However, it can be done, and, in fact, every year millions of tons of rare earth elements are mined and refined. (China produces 95 percent of the world's rare earths.)

The rare earth elements would have been useless to ancient peoples. They're not good for making pottery or jewelry or weapons. In the modern world, the rare earth elements are used in many "high-tech" products, such as color televisions, computer screens, lasers, cell phones, solar panels, spark plugs, camera lenses, x-ray screens, mercury lamps, lasers, medical imaging film, temperature-sensing optics, nuclear reactors, self-cleaning ovens and welding goggles. Without rare earths, "green" technology would not be possible. You can't have solar panels and wind turbines without mines that dig up and process rare earth ores.

These powdered rare earths were obtained from ores. They are not pure elements. Pure rare earths look shiny.

What makes rare earth elements so useful for technology? Basically two reasons: their **magnetism** and their ability to **fluoresce** *(flor-ESS)*.

Magnetism occurs when most of the electrons in a substance are spinning the same way. Remember those rules that electrons live by? The first rule was: "Spin!" When electrons pair up (another rule they live by) they always choose a partner who is spinning the opposite way. Pairing up

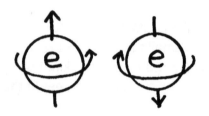

with their opposite "neutralizes" their spin, so the more <u>unpaired</u> electrons an element has, the more likely it is that the element will be magnetic. The elements in the middle of both the transition neighborhood (such as iron and cobalt) and in the lanthanide row (from neodymium to gadolinium) have the greatest number of unpaired electrons, so they are the most magnetic elements. (Promethium might be magnetic, but because it is radioactive it is not suitable for use in magnets.) How many unpaired electrons can a rare earth element have? The outer shell is an "f" shell, which can hold up to 14 electrons arranged into 7 pairs. The first 7 electrons get their own "seat" in the shell, then after that, the additional electrons have to start pairing up. So the maximum number of unpaired electrons is 7. This corresponds to the element gadolinium.

Neodymium and samarium might not have the maximum number of unpaired electrons, but they actually turn out to be the most useful for making magnets. On their own, however, their magnetism occurs only at low temperatures. They are mixed with transition metals such as iron, nickel or cobalt, which are magnetic at higher temperatures. One of the most common alloys of neodymium also has some boron in it: $Nd_2Fe_{14}B$. The crystal structure of this compound also happens to be very

A bracket containing a neodymium alloy magnet from the hard drive of a computer.

good for magnetism, so between the unpaired electrons and the crystal structure, this compound is so magnetic that even very tiny magnets are extremely powerful. This is handy for the electronics industry because if they had to use regular iron-cobalt magnets, cell phones would be ten times larger, and who would want to carry those around?! Computer hard drives also contain neodymium alloy magnets—another item where small size is a definite "plus."

Wow! These lanthanides turn out to be really important!

Not all rare earth alloy magnets are small. You will also find them in cordless tools, electric cars, loudspeakers, headphones, and MRI machines in hospitals. Perhaps the largest objects that contain rare earth magnets are the generators inside the huge wind turbines used to create electricity from wind. Looks like if you want green energy from wind, you need to mine those lanthanides!

Most of the rare earth elements also **fluoresce**. You see fluorescence *(flor-ESS-ence)* every time you look at a fluorescent bulb. (Fluorescent bulbs are usually very long or are spiral-shaped.) Magic markers used for highlighting textbooks also fluoresce. Laundry soaps often have fluorescent dyes that fool your eyes into thinking that the whites are "whiter than white." Other things fluoresce to some degree, but not enough for your eyes to be able to see it very well.

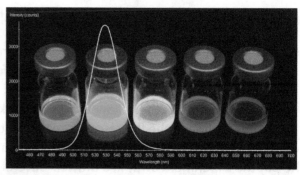

These liquids fluoresce when exposed to UV light. They are shown on a graph that gives the exact frequencies of light at the bottom. The spike in the graph corresponds to the intense glow of the green liquid. The others glow less, which is shown in the graph as a very low line.

Fluorescence is caused by "falling" electrons. When an electron (usually in the outer shell) gets "zapped" with some extra energy (ultra violet light, for example) the electron is "excited" into a higher energy state and "jumps" up to the next higher shell. However, it can't stay in that higher shell forever. Just as you must come back down when you jump into the air, so an electron can't stay at a higher energy level and must come back down to its normal level. When it falls back down, it releases the energy that it had absorbed. Often, the energy that is released doesn't look or act the same as the energy that went in. For example, when UV (ultra violet) light hits some atoms, the released energy isn't UV, but is a visible light such as green or red or blue. Scientists like to hit atoms with X-rays and watch what happens. X-rays are particularly useful in helping to figure out the molecular shape of a crystal or the identity of a mystery atom in the crystal. Heat can also cause electrons to jump. Think back to the discovery of helium. The scientists saw a striped pattern of colored lines in their spectrometer because the sun's heat was causing electrons in helium atoms to jump up and down, releasing their energy as bands of visible light. Each element has a unique pattern of electrons, and therefore a unique pattern of emitted light.

"What goes up must come back down." That includes you!

You may be wondering how an electron in an outer shell can jump to a higher shell. Is there an empty shell sitting around the outer one? Basically, yes. ALL the shells exist in every atom, whether they are filled or not. Imagine that each atom has an Atomizer pattern printed around it (but with many more orbitals than in our Atomizer activity). The rings are waiting for electrons to come and fill them. The outer rings of small atoms never get filled, of course. Large atoms such as uranium and plutonium use all, or at least most, of their rings.

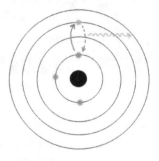

There are empty levels above the outer electron shell. One electron has jumped and then fallen back down, emiting light.

Now, back to the rare earth elements. **Europium** can fluoresce with either a red or blue light, depending on what other atoms are surrounding it. **Terbium** fluoresces bright green. These two elements are the key ingredients in making the colors you see on televisions and computer screens. Believe it or not, red, blue and green light can be combined to make any color—even yellow, brown, black and white.

Activity 8.1 Look at a screen

You will need a magnifier for this activity (at least 10x). Look at a computer or television screen while it is on. If your magnification is high enough, you will see that the image is nothing but red, green and blue dots or rectangles. Choose a place where you think it looks white or yellow or brown, then zoom in again. Is there really any white or yellow or brown? How can red, green and blue make white? Amazing!

Our Periodic Kingdom story ended with "Beware the Actinides!" because the elements in this row are all **radioactive**. Radioactivity was first discovered by a French scientist named Henri Becquerel in 1896. He was experimenting with rocks that were fluorescent and phosphorescent. (**Phosphorescence** *(foss-for-ESS-sense)* is when the electrons keeping falling for a number of minutes, causing the "glow in the dark" phenomenon.) Becquerel would cover a photographic plate with black paper then allow sunlight to strike the rocks, which would fluoresce. He hoped the fluorescence would go through the black paper and make an image of the photographic plate. When weather turned cloudy one day, he put the experiment away in a drawer. Several days later he opened the drawer and was shocked by what he saw. The photographic film had a very clear image of the rocks on it. How could that have happened in a dark drawer without any light? Becquerel correctly guessed that something in the rocks was giving off a type of energy that did not depend on sunlight. He knew that the rocks contained the element uranium, and supposed that it might be the uranium that was doing this. Becquerel then handed off the investigation to Maire Curie.

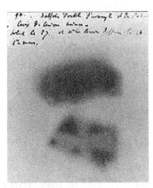
This is Becquerel's image of the rocks in the drawer.

Marie Curie in her lab in Paris.

Marie Sklodowska had come to France from Poland. While studying and working in Paris, Marie and met and married Pierre Curie, another brilliant scientist who was discovering many new things. Marie began studying a mineral ore called **pitchblende** that was known to contain uranium. She boiled samples of pitchblende for several years, trying to get all the uranium out. After the uranium was gone, the remaining minerals still gave off rays of energy. This led her to believe there was another element still in the rock that was capable of producing the same rays of mysterious energy. Eventually she managed to isolate a small amount of a new element. She decided to name it **polonium** after her native country, Poland. She named this new type of energy **radioactivity**.

After the polonium had been extracted from the rocks, they STILL gave off radioactivity! Could there be a third radioactive element? Sure enough, there was. When she finally isolated this third radioactive element, she named it **radium**, and calculated that it was 200 times more radioactive than uranium. Good thing she'd been wearing protective gear while... oops—she hadn't been wearing any protection at all. No one at that time had any idea how harmful radiation was. They thought it was just an interesting thing that some elements did. Amazingly, Marie lived until the age of 60 before she died of a cancerous illness caused by the massive amount of radiation she had been exposing herself to for years.

Most of the chemical properties of an atom come from the electrons in its outer shell. Radioactivity, though, is all about the nucleus.

The atomic mass of [the most common form] of uranium is 238. That means if you add up all the protons and all the neutrons, you will get a total of 238 particles. That's a huge nucleus! In fact, it is so huge that it has trouble staying together. It's like a big crumbly cookie; little bits can break off easily. When an atom's nucleus

begins to crumble, it doesn't drop crumbs or chocolate chips, of course. It flings out protons, neutrons, and rays of dangerous energy. "Radioactivity" is the name for those particles flying out of the nucleus.

The particles that are ejected from the nucleus are classified into three groups: alpha, beta, and gamma. Those are the first three letters of the Greek alphabet, so it's like saying A, B and C. Alpha particles consist of two protons and two neutrons. Beta particles are basically high energy electrons, and gamma particles are made of the same kind of energy as light (electromagnetic energy) but carry a dangerously high level of that energy. Let's focus on alpha particles for a few minutes because they turn out to be part of the process of one element turning into another. (The alchemist's dream comes true!)

An alpha particle is made of two protons and two neutrons. If this particle can capture two electrons, it will then have exactly the same structure as a helium atom. Electrons are pretty much everywhere all the time, so it is not hard for an apha particle to find two electrons. Once it has captured the electrons, it is no longer an alpha particle but has become a genuine helium atom. This is what eventually happens to all alpha particles—they become helium atoms. So when geologists find helium atoms inside rocks or between rock layers, they assume that there was once radioactivity in that area.

These symbols are used as warnings about radioactivity.

What happens to a uranium atom if it ejects an alpha particle? The nucleus no longer has 92 protons; it now has only 90. Since the number of protons defines what element an atom is, the uranium is no longer uranium, but has turned into element

An alpha particle that has captured two electrons and turned into a helium atom

number 90, thorium. Thorium is still radioactive, however, and will eventually eject an alpha particle. When it does, the nucleus will no longer have 90 protons, but will have only 88. Thorium has turned into element 88, radium. If this happens again, radium will lose two protons and turn into radon, 86. Radon is radioactive and could lose two protons and become element 84, polonium. Polonium is also radioactive, as Marie Curie found out, and is capable of giving off an alpha particle. If polonium loses two protons, it will turn into 82, lead. Lead has a stable nucleus and is not radioactive. Lead won't turn into anthing else. Lead is a stopping point for this process that we call radioactive "decay."

The entire actinide row is radioactive, but as we've seen already, there are other elements on the table that are radioactive, as well. Starting with 84, polonium, all the higher elements are radioactive. There are also two radioactive elements with numbers less than 84: technetium, 43, and promethium, 61. So we can say that all actinides are radioactive, but not all radioactive elements are actinides.

Uranium is generally considered to be the last **naturally occurring** element on the Periodic Table. (We must say "generally" because recently there have been reports of very tiny amounts of neptunium being discovered in uranium ore. However, most science books still list uranium as the last naturally occurring element.) Plutonium and the other actinides can't be dug out of the ground. They simply do not exist anywhere in nature. They are completely man-made elements. Man-made? Can elements be manufactured? Yes, if you have a nuclear reactor and a particle accelerator.

We just saw the process of radioactive "decay," where elements lost pairs of protons and changed into lower elements, all the way down to lead. What would happen if you could <u>add</u> protons? Because elements are defined by the number of protons they have, if you added a proton to uranium, it would no longer be uranium. Until the 1940s, there was no way to add protons to atoms. Then, during World War II, scientists in both Germany and the USA discovered how to make machines that would shoot protons at atomic nuclei. Unfortunately, the reason they wanted to do this was to make nuclear bombs. However, aside from bombs,

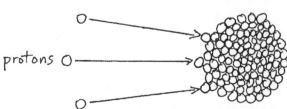

this technology proved to be useful because it could allow chemists to make many new elements. They would shoot protons at an atom that was already very large, such as thorium or protactinium or uranium, and hope that some of the protons would stick to the nucleus. They were very careful

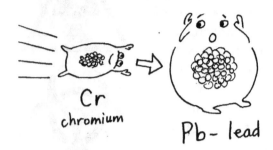

Cr
chromium

Pb - lead

Sometimes two medium-sized atoms are crashed together in the hopes that they will stick and make a super heavy element. To make 106, chromium (24) and lead (82) were used. The math works: 82 + 24 = 106

about their technique so that they knew exactly how many protons were sticking. As the number of protons grew, so did the number of new elements. Each time they got one more proton to stick, they created a new element. These new elements needed names, and this ended up being a way to honor the memories of great scientists such as Marie Curie, Albert Einstein, Enrico Fermi, Dmitri Mendeleyev, and Alfred Nobel. Some of the new actinides were named after the places where they were created, such as Berkeley, California, USA (berkelium, californium and americium), hassium (Hesse, Germany), dubnium (Dubna, Russia) and hafnium (Hafnia, the old name for Copenhagen, Denmark).

A big problem with these super heavy elements is that their nuclei are too large to ever be stable. They are doomed to fall apart eventually. However, some super heavy nuclei are stable enough to stay in existence for weeks or months, long enough that scientists can observe them and determine some of their chemical properties. They always turn out to be similar to the elements that are above them in the same column. Other super heavy elements fall apart after a few seconds, or even a fraction of a second. They wink out of existence before any tests can be done on them, so we know much less about them.

Scientists made so many new elements that they filled up the actinide row and had to go back to the bottom row of the transition block (the ghost town in the Periodic Kingdom, where the residents are rarely

seen). When someone claimed to have "discovered" a new element, it would take a long time, perhaps even years, to verify that they had actually done so. Experiments and data would have to be published so that scientists all over the world would be able to read about what had been done and agree that a new element had indeed been made. Only after the discoverer's claims were judged to be valid would a name be chosen for the new element.

Naming an element is often complicated by disagreements about who was first to make it. For example, Russia and America argued over element 106 for a long time before the international chemistry naming group, IUPAC, decided that America had been first. Whoever discovers an element gets to name it, so, of course, the Americans choose to name it after an American scientist. They chose Glenn Seaborg, who has been given credit for discovering, or helping to discover, plutonium, americium, curium, berkelium, californium, einsteinium, fermium, mendelevium and nobelium. (As you might guess, Seaborg's lab is located in Berkeley, California.)

When chemists realized that it might be possible to make a lot more new elements, they began labeling the empty blocks in the bottom row with temporary, fictional names made from Latin and Greek words. For example, before 106 was named seaborgium, it was called "unnilhexium." ("Un" is Latin for "one," "nil" is Greek for "zero," and "hex" is Greek for "six.") There are still many Periodic Table images on the Internet that have some temporary names such as UUT, UUP, UUS, and UUO. However, the most up-to-date tables will show the decisions made by the IUPAC up to 2015, and will display the actual names of the elements: darmstadtium, roentgenium, copernicium, nihonium, flerovium, moscovium, livermorium, tennessine, and oganesson.

Activity 8.2   A video about Marie Curie and the discovery of polonium and radium

Marie Curie discovered polonium in 1898 and then radium soon after. Marie's life story is amazing and inspiring. There are several videos about her posted on YouTube playlist.

Activity 8.3   A virtual field trip

The professors who made the Periodic Table of Videos filmed a trip they made to Ytterby, Sweden, to find the famous mine that was the source of the mineral ore that allowed the discovery of Yttrium, Terbium, Erbium and Ytterbium.

The mnemonic story below will make more sense if you've seen this video first. Watch "Ytterby Road Trip" on The Elements playlist on the YouTube channel.

Activity 8.4   Memorize the Lanthanides and Actinides

This activity is optional, of course. But for those of you intent on memorizing the table, perhaps this little mnemonic story might help. (You can always make up your own story, too!)

The Lanthanides are for those who are SERIOUS about learning the whole table.
(cerium)

Begin by PRAISING NEODYMIUM for its wonderful magnetic properties. Then tell this
(praseodymium)   (Neodymium magnets are extremely strong.)

story: "I PROMised to take SAM to EUROPE so he could see the famous mine where
(promethium)   (samarium) (europium)

(This)
Johan GADOLIN discovered TERBIUM. When we got there, he said, "DYS HOLE isn't
(gadolinium)   (dysprosium) (holmium)

what I was expecting! I was expecting an URBan area with "inTHULated" buildings.
(the mine was a big disapointment)   (erbium)   (thulium)   (It's cold in Sweden!)

Let's leave YTTERBY and go back to the row with the LOOT! (meaning the row that has gold in it)
(ytterbium)   (lutetium)

For the Actinide Series, you need to be THORoughly PROTECTed because they're all
(thorium)   (protactinium)

radioactive. URANIUM, NEPTUNIUM and PLUTONIUM are the most famous members

of this row because they were used by AMERICA to make atomic bombs. Marie CURIE
(americium)   (curium)

would have loved to visit BERKELEY, CALIFORNIA to see the scientists make
(berkelium)   (californium)

EINSTEINIUM and FERMIUM. But she, MENDELEYEV and Alfred NOBEL all died when
(named for Enrico Fermi)   (mendelevium)   (nobelium)

elements beyond uranium were still folkLORE.
(lawrencium)

Activity 8.5   Four new elements are named

Go to periodicvideos.com and watch the video about the naming of four new elements.

Activity 8.6   "Odd one out" (Which one of these doesn't belong?)

Now that we've finished our tour of the Periodic Kingdom, we can do an activity where you use your knowledge of the table to try to figure out which element doesn't belong in the group.

EXAMPLE 1:   Ne   Ar   Xe   Cl   (Chlorine does not belong because it is not a noble gas.)
EXAMPLE 2:   Sn   Bi   Ti   Al   (Titanium does not belong because it is not a true metal.)

1) Ca   Sc   Co   Ag

2) Rb   Be   K   Cs

3) S   C   K   P

4) Cd   Cm   Cr   Cu

5) Pm   Sm   Tm   Fm

6) Na   Ca   Ra   Ba

7) Pt   Pu   Pa   Np

8) B   Ge   Br   Si

9) Rh   Re   Rn   Ru

10) Te   Tb   Eu   Er

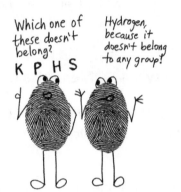

Activity 8.7   "Who am I?"

Figure out which lanthanide or actinide is being described.

1) I fluoresce bright green, so I am used in televisions and computer screens. _____

2) I was made by smashing a chromium atom into a lead atom. _____

3) I am the only radioactive lanthanide. _____

4) I am the last naturally occurring actinide. Elements above me are man-made. _____

5) If I were to lose an alpha particle, I would turn into uranium. _____

6) We are used to make very strong magnets. (The element right between us might also be magnetic, but it can't be used because it is dangerous.) _____ and _____

7) I was named after the man who invented the Periodic Table. _____

8) I can fluoresce either bright red or bright blue, depending on the atoms around me. _____

9) I was named after a mine in Sweden where I was first discovered. My name does not begin with Y, nor does it begin with T. _____

10) I was named after the US state where my discoverer lived and worked. _____

ANSWER KEY

ANSWER KEY

CHAPTER 1
Answers will vary for the activities not listed here.

Activity 1.5:
1) C= 2, O= 6   2) 3   3) 2   4) Si= 2, O= 8

Activity 1.6:
1) nobelium   2) vanadium   3) gadolinium   4) polonium   5) einsteinium   6) berkelium
7) tellurium   8) scandium   9) ytterbium   10) niobium   11) tin   12) holmium
13) neptunium   14) curium   15) mercury   16) tantalum   17) cerium   18) gallium
19) selenium   20) bromine   21) iridium   22) thorium   23) nickel   24) cobalt   25) chlorine

CHAPTER 2
Activity 2.2
1) phosphorus   2) fluorine   3) calcium   4) gallium   5) titanium   6) silicon
7) rhodium   8) iodine   9) scandium   10) palladium   11) tin   12) sulfur
13) chlorine   14) argon   15) nitrogen   16) hydrogen   17) carbon   18) boron
19) potassium   20) xenon

Activity 2.6
1) Why did the mouse say, "Cheep, cheep," when the bird's cage fell apart?
He was filling in for the bird who had the day off.
2) What do you get when you cross a vampire with a mouse?   A terrified cat!
3) What were Batman and Robin's new names after they were run over by a car?   Flatman and Ribbon!

CHAPTER 3
Activity 3.4
Nitrogen: $1s^2\ 2s^2\ 2p^3$
Sulfur: $1s^2\ 2s^2\ 2p^6\ 3s^2\ 3p^4$
Neon: $1s^2\ 2s^2\ 2p^6$
Chlorine: $1s^2\ 2s^2\ 2p^6\ 3s^2\ 3p^5$
Lithium: $1s^2\ 2s^1$
Boron: $1s^2\ 2s^2\ 2p^1$
Silicon: $1s^2\ 2s^2\ 2p^6\ 3s^2\ 3p^2$
Fluorine: $1s^2\ 2s^2\ 2p^5$

Activity 3.5
Ag-47	H-1	Os-76
Am-95	He-2	P-15
At-85	I-53	S-16
As-33	In-49	Se-34

Activity 3.6
1) Be   2) N   3) Na   4) S   5) P   6) Ca   Challenge: Fe

Activity 3.6
Just use the Periodic Table as your guide. It tells you what all the symbols are!

CHAPTER 4
Activity 4.1

 Could be -2 or +6. Choose the smaller number, 2.

O -2 S -2 Kr 0

Mg $+2$ Br -1 K $+1$

C ±4 P -3 Ba $+2$

Sc $+3$ Si ±4 Li $+1$

Activity 4.2

B: $+3$ P: -3 O: -2 H $+1$

S: -2 Mg: $+2$ Al: $+3$ Li $+1$

Ne: 0 C: ±4 N: -3 Fl: -1

Li (lithium) +1 — Li·
B (boron) +3 — B:
I (iodine) -1 — ·I:
N (nitrogen) -3 — ·N:

C (carbon) +4 — ·C:
Be (beryllium) +2 — Be:
K (potassium) +1 — K·
S (sulfur) -2 — ·S:

Activity 4.3
1) B- boron (boring)   2) Ar- argon ("are gone")   3) Ba- barium ("bury 'em")
4) Es- einsteinium (after Einstein)   5) Pu- plutonium (named after Pluto, which is way out there!)
6) Eu- europium (named after Europe)   7) Fe- iron (as in ironing clothes)   8) Kr- krypton
9) Hg - mercury   10) Cf- californium   11) Si- silicon ("silly con")   12) Ni- nickel
13) Po- polonium ("polo" like field hockey played while riding horses)   14) Os- osmium (sounds like "Oz")

CHAPTER 5 does not have any activities that need answers.

CHAPTER 6
Activity 6.4
1) PLaSTiC   2) GaSOLiNe   3) PrOPaNe   4) AsPHAlt   5) AlCoHoL   6) BUCKY BAlL
7) CaFFEINe   8) AmInO AcId   9) FAtS   10) PaRaFFIn   11) PoLYEsTeR   12) GLuCoSe
13) HaIr   14) GLuTeN   15) NYLON   16) ArTiFICIAl FLaVORS   17) PLaNT FIBeR
Trivia question: The letters J and Q do not appear in any element symbol, assuming you are using the most up-to-date version of the table. Uuq was a symbol until recently, so if you have an old table, you might see a Q.

Activity 6.5
1) b   2) d   3) a   4) noble gases   5) alkali   6) halogens   7) S   8) C   9) N   10) He
11) sand   12) salt   13) bleach   14) Teflon   15) plaster   16) c   17) e   18) protons
19) d   20) c   BONUS: 1) sulfur   2) 146   3) 38

CHAPTER 7
Activity 7.4
1) gallium, Ga   2) arsenic, As   3) lead, Pb   4) antimony, Sb   5) indium, In   6) tin, Sn
7) thallium, Tl   8) bismuth, Bi   9) tellurium, Te   10) aluminum, Al   11) boron, B   12) silicon, Si

CHAPTER 8
Activity 8.6
1) Ca (not transition metal)   2) Be (not alkali metal)   3) K (not non-metal)
4) Cm (not transition metal)   5) Fm (not lanthanide)   6) Na (not alkali earth metal)
7) Pt (not actinide)   8) Br (not semi-metal)   9) Rn (not transition metal)   10) Te (not lanthanide)

Activity 8.7
1) Tb, terbium   2) Sg, seaborgium   3) Pm, promethium   4) U, uranium   5) Pu, plutonium
6) Nd and Sm, neodymium and samarium   7) Md, mendelevium   8) Eu, europium
9) Er, erbium   10) Cf, californium

The following pages are a preview of:

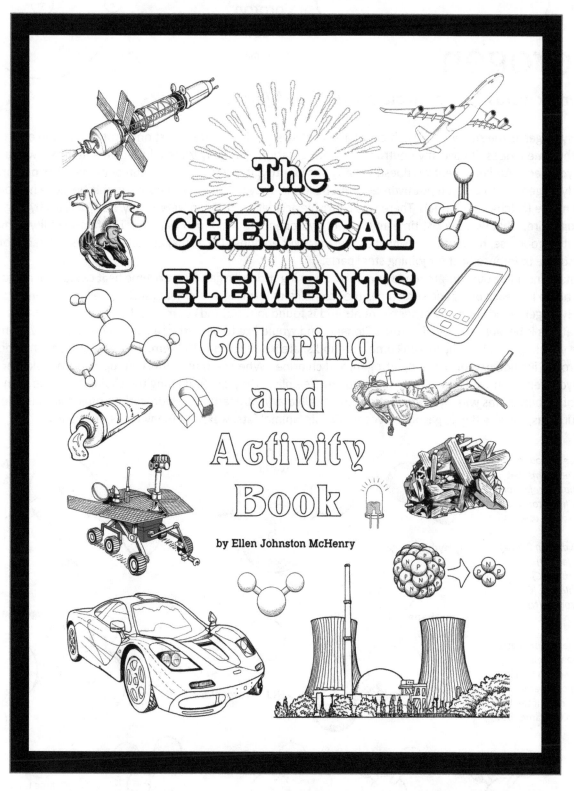

If you find these coloring pages helpful, the full book (all 118 elements) is available at your favorite book distributor.   ISBN 978-1-7374763-0-6

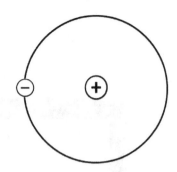

1 proton
1 electron

Atomic mass: 1.0

Hydrogen

From Greek words "hydro" (water) and "genes" (make)

Hydrogen is the smallest and lightest of all the elements. It is made of just one proton and one electron. Most of the time it doesn't have any neutrons. On rare occasions when hydrogen does gain a neutron, we call it "heavy hydrogen." Adding a neutron doesn't change its identity; it will still be hydrogen because it has one proton.

Hydrogen is a gas. If you put hydrogen into balloons, they will float. But don't try this because hydrogen is very flammable (catches fire easily). There was a terrible accident in 1937 in New Jersey, USA, when a hydrogen-filled blimp caught fire. That was the last time anyone put hydrogen into a blimp or balloon. The flammability of hydrogen can be put to good use, however, by using it as fuel in rocket engines. On a smaller scale, welders use tanks of hydrogen as a source of intense heat for joining steel parts.

Stars, including our sun, are made primarily of burning hydrogen gas. The extreme heat causes the hydrogen atoms to bump into each other and sometimes they combine to form larger elements such as helium, lithium or sodium.

Hydrogen bonds to many other elements and is found in thousands of molecules. The reason it likes to bond to other atoms is because its one electron is "lonely" and would like to be part of a pair. There are many atoms who would be very happy to have hydrogen come over and share its electron with them. Atoms that frequently bond with hydrogen include oxygen, carbon, nitrogen, and chlorine. When carbon atoms join together to make very long chains, hydrogen atoms will attach themselves to any free place they can find along the chain. This type of molecule (a chain of carbon atoms with hydrogens attached) is called a "hydrocarbon." Hydrocarbon molecules include methane (natural gas), octane (liquid gasoline), vegetable oils, animal fats, wax, and many types of plastics.

You can assign your own colors to the atoms, but here is what a professional scientific illustrator would be most likely to use:

White: Hydrogen (blank)
Red: Oxygen (O)
Black: Carbon (C)
Green: Chlorine (Cl)
Blue: Nitrogen (N)

The hydrogens look pretty big in these models. They are actually much smaller than these other atoms, but it looks nicer if the balls are close to the same size.

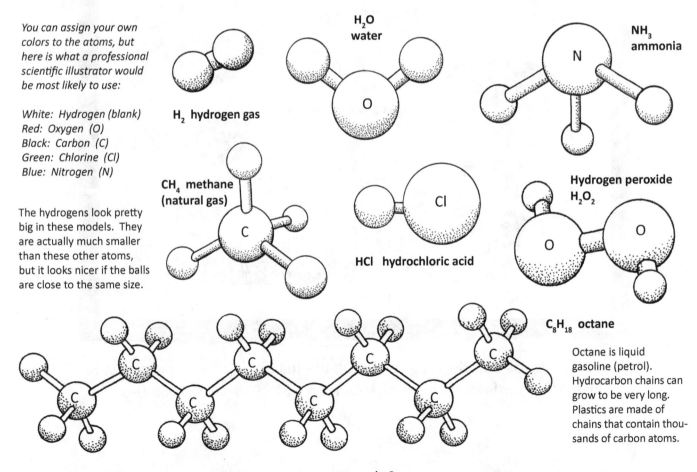

H_2 hydrogen gas

H_2O
water

NH_3
ammonia

CH_4 methane
(natural gas)

HCl hydrochloric acid

Hydrogen peroxide
H_2O_2

C_8H_{18} octane

Octane is liquid gasoline (petrol). Hydrocarbon chains can grow to be very long. Plastics are made of chains that contain thousands of carbon atoms.

sample-2

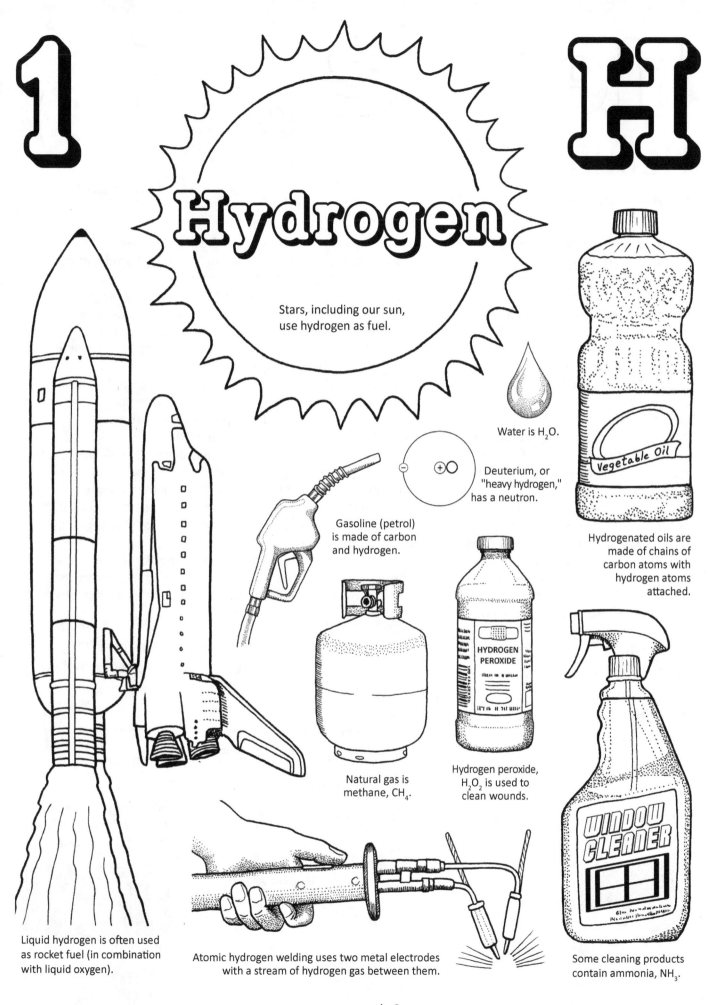

1

H

Hydrogen

Stars, including our sun, use hydrogen as fuel.

Water is H_2O.

Deuterium, or "heavy hydrogen," has a neutron.

Gasoline (petrol) is made of carbon and hydrogen.

Natural gas is methane, CH_4.

Hydrogen peroxide, H_2O_2 is used to clean wounds.

Hydrogenated oils are made of chains of carbon atoms with hydrogen atoms attached.

Liquid hydrogen is often used as rocket fuel (in combination with liquid oxygen).

Atomic hydrogen welding uses two metal electrodes with a stream of hydrogen gas between them.

Some cleaning products contain ammonia, NH_3.

He

Helium

From the Greek word for sun: "helios"

2 protons
2 neutrons
2 electrons

Atomic mass: 4.0

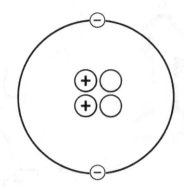

Helium was first discovered in the sun, which is why it was named after the Greek god of the sun, Helios. Scientists in the 1860s were beginning to use a new tool, called the spectrometer, to look at light produced by various things, including the elements as they were burned. They noticed that each burning element seemed to give off a unique light pattern, almost like a fingerprint, by which it could be identified. When they saw a new light pattern as they looked at the sun, they knew it must be a new element. In 1868, Norman Lockyer announced the discovery of a new element that he had named "helium." Then, in 1895, William Ramsay discovered helium in a sample of rock that contained the element uranium. Helium was not just in the sun, but on earth as well! It was later found that helium is produced as uranium atoms break apart, or "decay."

The element helium is a very light gas. Unlike hydrogen, helium is not flammable. Put a spark to helium and nothing happens. This makes it very safe to put in blimps, party balloons, and weather balloons. Helium is so unreactive that it can be put into rocket engines that are filled with hydrogen. It is also used as a "shield gas" in arc welding, surrounding and insulating the dangerously hot arc of electricity.

Another place the safety of helium comes in handy is in air tanks used by scuba divers. The air around us is mostly nitrogen, with some oxygen mixed in. If divers take normal air down with them, the nitrogen can do something harmful. If the divers come up too quickly, the nitrogen can bubble into their blood, much like bubbles appear when you open a carbonated beverage. Bubbles in your blood is not good! This dangerous condition is called "the bends." (Divers hurt so much they bend over with the pain.) However, if helium is used in place of nitrogen, divers can come back up without having to worry about getting "the bends."

Helium has other technological uses. A mixture of helium and neon is used in red lasers, the kind that are used to read bar codes at check outs in stores. Extremely cold liquid helium is used in machines and devices that need extremely powerful magnets, such as MRI machines in hospitals, and the particle accelerators used by physicists to do experiments with electrons, protons, and neutrons.

Helium atoms don't bond to other atoms. They float around by themselves.

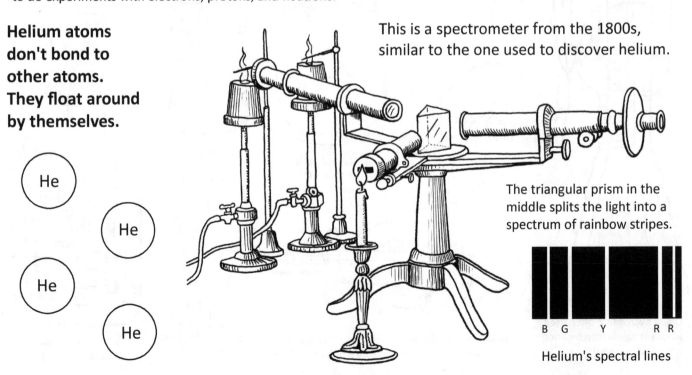

This is a spectrometer from the 1800s, similar to the one used to discover helium.

The triangular prism in the middle splits the light into a spectrum of rainbow stripes.

B G Y R R

Helium's spectral lines

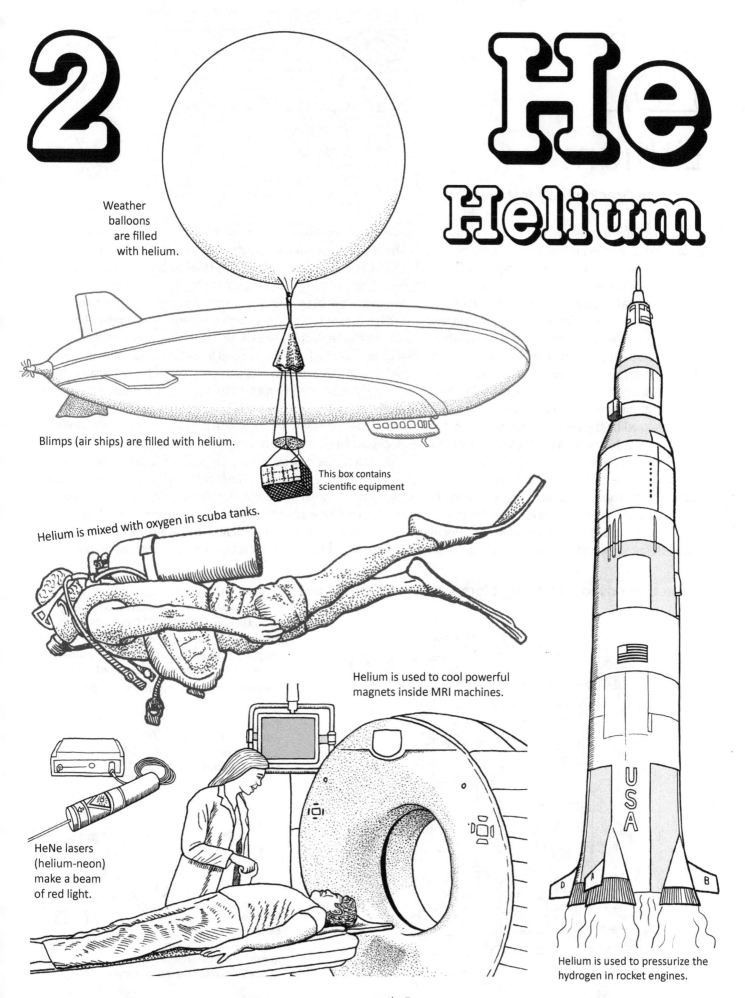

2 He

Helium

Weather balloons are filled with helium.

Blimps (air ships) are filled with helium.

This box contains scientific equipment

Helium is mixed with oxygen in scuba tanks.

Helium is used to cool powerful magnets inside MRI machines.

HeNe lasers (helium-neon) make a beam of red light.

USA

Helium is used to pressurize the hydrogen in rocket engines.

 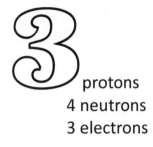 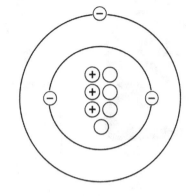

Li

Lithium

3 protons
4 neutrons
3 electrons

Atomic mass: 6.94

From the Greek word for stone: "lithos"

Lithium is most well-known for its use in long-life batteries, but it's also used in lubricants, fuels, metal alloys, glass making, and even medicines. Some of its useful qualities come from its electron configuration. Do you see that one lonely electron in the outer ring? It's very "unhappy" because it doesn't have a partner to pair up with. The two electrons in the inner ring are paired up, and are therefore very content. The unpaired electron in the outer ring is so "unhappy" that it would rather go off and be part of another atom than stay where it is. Some atoms, like fluorine, chlorine, and bromine (members of the halogen family) are desperate to grab an extra electron that doesn't belong to them, so if they run into a lithium atom, it's a perfect match. Molecules like LiF, LiCl and LiBr are relatively easy to make in a lab. LiF, lithium fluoride, takes the form of a clear crystal which can be used in optical lenses and in radiation detectors. LiCl, lithium chloride, is a white powder that is used in fireworks and emergency flares because it produces a bright reddish-pink flame. LiBr, lithium bromide, can be used to trap moisture in air conditioning systems.

Lithium atoms will bond to small groups of atoms, such as the carbonate ion, CO_3^{2-}. Lithium carbonate, Li_2CO_3, is used by the ceramics industry to make glazes and tile adhesives, by the metal industry to process aluminum, by the glass industry to make ovenware, by the pharmaceutical industry to make medicines, and by the battery industry to make long-life lithium ion batteries. Lithium bonds well to the hydroxide ion, OH^-, to form LiOH, a compound that can remove carbon dioxide from the air that circulates inside an airplane. Lithium will also bond to metals such as aluminum, copper and manganese, making lightweight alloys (metal mixtures) that are used to make airplanes.

Lithium atoms are never found alone in nature. To get a pure sample of lithium, a strong electrical current must be used. Pure lithium looks like a silvery metal and is so light it will float on water. It will also react with the water, trying to get rid of that lonely electron, and this will cause it to look like it is burning on top of the water.

When Li bonds to F, Cl, or Br, it forms a crystal shape:

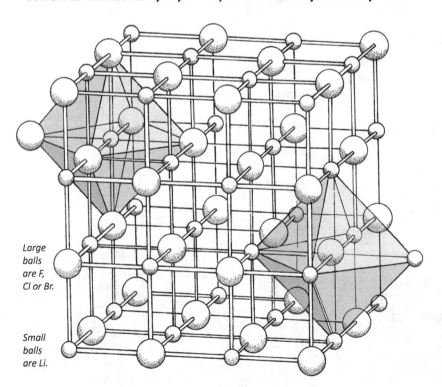

Large balls are F, Cl or Br.

Small balls are Li.

When two Li atoms connect to a CO_3, they don't bond in the way that C and O do. (The sticks represent bonds.) Instead, the Li atoms are held in place by electrical attraction. The positively charged Li atoms (ions) are attracted to the negatively charged oxygen atoms in the CO_3.

This Li_2CO_3 molecule will join with others just like it to form a crystal-like structure.

Red: Oxygen (O)
Black: Carbon (C)
You can decide what color to make lithium. A professional artist would probably use purple or pink.

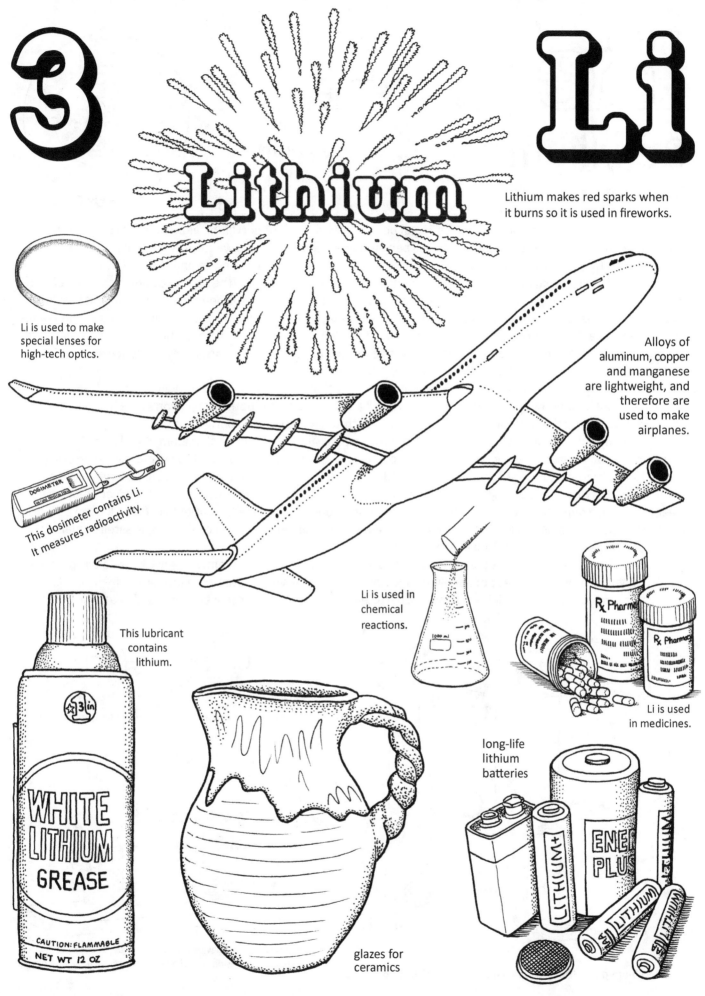

3

Lithium

Li

Lithium makes red sparks when it burns so it is used in fireworks.

Li is used to make special lenses for high-tech optics.

Alloys of aluminum, copper and manganese are lightweight, and therefore are used to make airplanes.

This dosimeter contains Li. It measures radioactivity.

Li is used in chemical reactions.

This lubricant contains lithium.

Li is used in medicines.

long-life lithium batteries

WHITE LITHIUM GREASE

CAUTION: FLAMMABLE

NET WT 12 OZ

glazes for ceramics

Be
Beryllium

From the mineral "beryl"

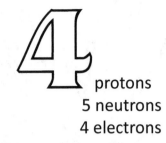

4
protons
5 neutrons
4 electrons

Atomic mass: 9.01

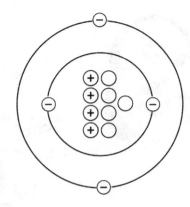

Beryllium's name comes from the mineral beryl. Beryl is made of beryllium, aluminum, silicon and oxygen, with this chemical formula: $Be_3Al_2(SiO_3)_6$. When beryl is made into a gemstone, we call it an emerald. Beryllium was first extracted from beryl in 1828 by two people working independently, one in France and one in Germany.

Beryllium is the smallest and lightest member of the alkali earth family (the second column from the left on the Periodic Table). This means that it has two electrons in its outer shell. This is better than just one, but beryllium would prefer to have 8 electrons in its outer shell, so it will easily give up its electrons to another atom or group of atoms. Oxygen makes a natural pairing, since it is looking for two electrons to complete its shell. BeO, beryllium oxide, is used to make parts for rocket engines, as a protective coating on telescope mirrors, as semiconductors in radios, and for ceramic parts in microwave devices, vacuum tubes, and lasers.

Pure beryllium can also be very useful, due to the fact that x-rays will go right through very small atoms. If you want to put a "window" in a vacuum tube, you need a substance that is both strong (won't cave in when the pressure drops inside the tube) and yet will let x-rays pass through. Beryllium is perfect for this.

When a little bit of beryllium is added to another metal, such as copper or aluminum, it makes it stronger. Beryllium bronze is made of 2% beryllium and 98% copper. The strength of beryllium bronze makes it an excellent choice for the manufacturing of parts such as heavy duty springs, which must maintain their shape even under a lot of stress. Beryllium bronze is special in another way, too. It won't create a spark if it strikes another metal, even steel. There are some places where sparks can be very dangerous, and you don't want to take the risk that your tool will start a fire or cause an explosion. Beryllium bronze tools are used on oil rigs, in coal mines, in satellite manufacturing, and by people who repair MRI machines.

Beryllium's claim to fame is that it was used to discover neutrons. In 1932, James Chadwick shot alpha particles (nuclei of helium atoms) at a piece of beryllium, and unknown particles (neutrons) were produced. Beryllium can be used as a source of neutrons for lab experiments, particle accelerators, nuclear power plants, and in atomic bombs.

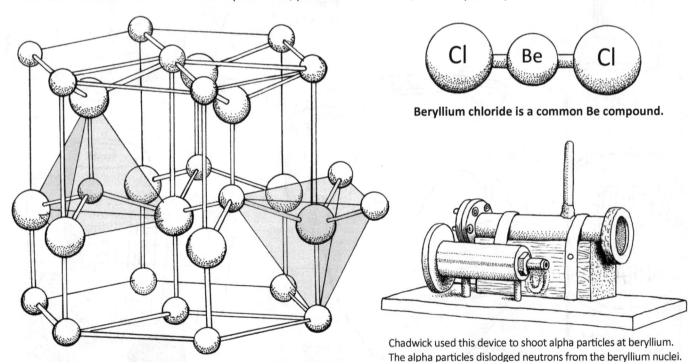

Beryllium chloride is a common Be compound.

Beryllium oxide (BeO) will make a crystal lattice shape.

Chadwick used this device to shoot alpha particles at beryllium.
The alpha particles dislodged neutrons from the beryllium nuclei.

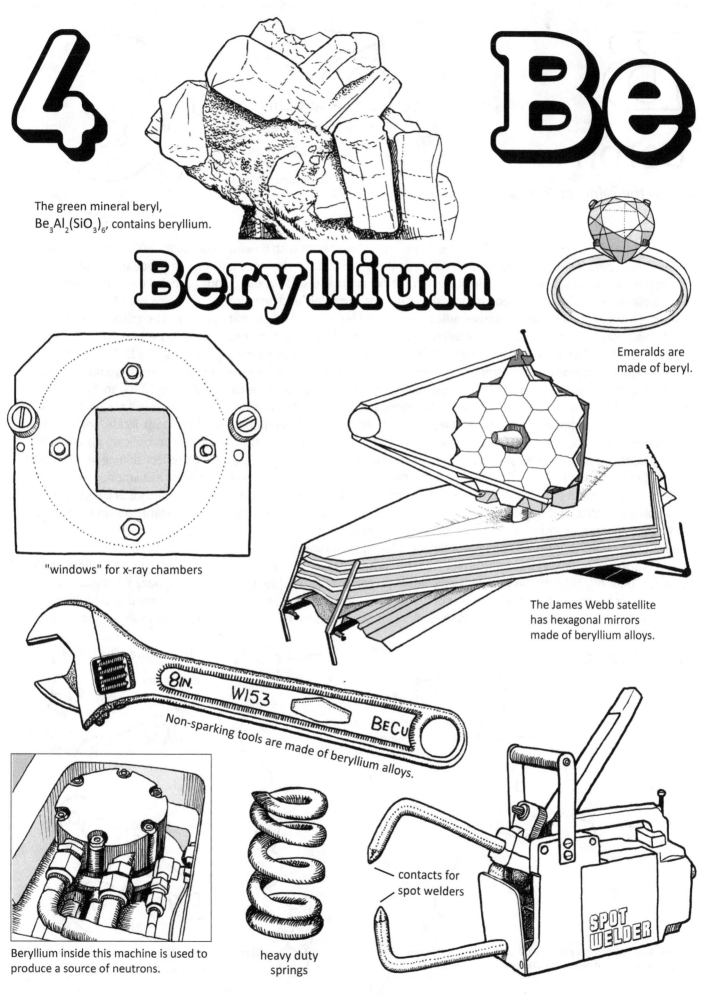

4

Be

The green mineral beryl, $Be_3Al_2(SiO_3)_6$, contains beryllium.

Beryllium

Emeralds are made of beryl.

"windows" for x-ray chambers

The James Webb satellite has hexagonal mirrors made of beryllium alloys.

8IN. W153 BeCu

Non-sparking tools are made of beryllium alloys.

Beryllium inside this machine is used to produce a source of neutrons.

heavy duty springs

contacts for spot welders

SPOT WELDER

Boron

From the mineral "borax"

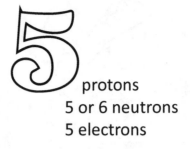

protons
5 or 6 neutrons
5 electrons

Atomic mass: 10.81

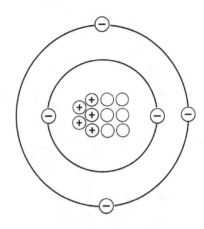

Boron is happy with either 5 or 6 neutrons. It is shown here with 6 neutrons because 80% of all boron atoms have 6. However, if it loses a neutron, it's no big deal. In many atoms, losing a neutron IS a big deal, and this will make the nucleus unstable. (Unstable nuclei tend to fall apart and spit out dangerous particles that can cause damage to plants and animals.) Boron atoms with 5 neutrons can safely add one more. The atoms with 5 neutrons are useful in nuclear power plants that use radioactive (unstable) elements that emit neutrons when they fall apart. Rods containing boron atoms are placed in areas where dangerous free neutrons need to be safely absorbed.

The fact that boron can have either 5 or 6 neutrons explains why its mass is listed as 10.81. The mass is the total number of protons and neutrons in the nucleus. Since boron can have either 5 or 6 neutrons, we must look at as many boron atoms as we can, and then calculate the average. The average turns out to be 10.81, so this is listed as the official atomic mass. But you'll never find a boron atom with 10.81 things in its nucleus! It will always be 10 or 11.

Boron is added to glass to make it less likely to shatter at high temperatures. This "borosilicate" glass is ideal for both kitchens and science labs. (The glassware called Pyrex® is borosilicate glass.) Tiny borosilicate glass beads can be added to paint that is used to put lines on roads. The glass beads in the paint will reflect shining headlights at night. Boron is added to glass that will be spun into the very thin fibers that make fiberglass insulation.

A very useful property of boron is that it won't burn (meaning combustion in the presence of oxygen). Boron compounds, such as zinc borate, can be sprayed onto fabric or wood to make them fire resistant. Boron's presence in fiberglass increases its resistance to fire as well as making the fibers stronger. When boron is used in fireworks, the atoms don't "burn" but they do heat up, showing a bright green color.

Boron is usually extracted from the mineral "borax" ($Na_2B_4O_7 - 10H_2O$). Borax is used to make laundry washing powder. (Kids might know this powder as the stuff you combine with white glue to make an oozy substance known as "slime" or "goop.") The cleaning power of borax is useful in medicine, too. Borax can be turned into boric acid, H_3BO_3, and put into germ-fighting eye washes. Borax is poisonous to insects and is often used in ant and roach traps.

Boric acid, H_3BO_3

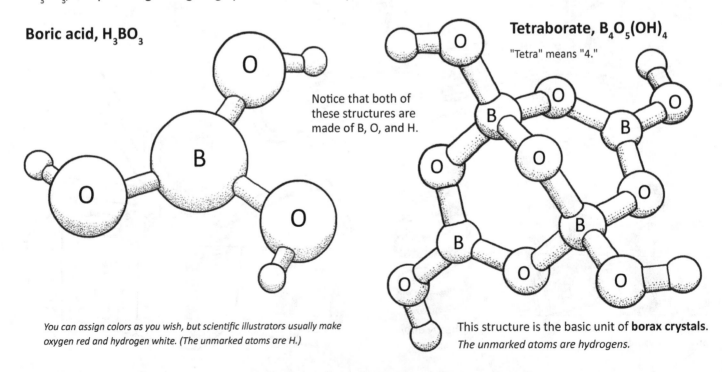

Notice that both of these structures are made of B, O, and H.

Tetraborate, $B_4O_5(OH)_4$

"Tetra" means "4."

You can assign colors as you wish, but scientific illustrators usually make oxygen red and hydrogen white. (The unmarked atoms are H.)

This structure is the basic unit of **borax crystals**.
The unmarked atoms are hydrogens.

5

It's fun to watch borax crystals grow on top of shapes you make.

B

Ulexite is a boron mineral with interesting optical properties.

Boron

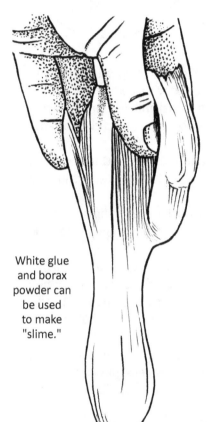

White glue and borax powder can be used to make "slime."

borosilicate glass

1000 ml

Borax washing powder

BORAX

DETERGENT BOOSTER

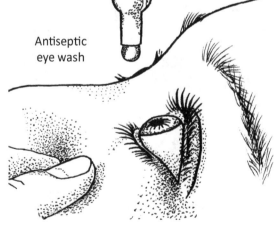

Antiseptic eye wash

Fiberglass insulation

Ant poison

Carbon

From the Latin word for charcoal: "carbo"

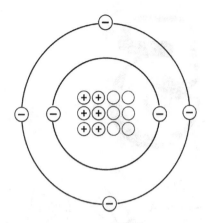

6 protons
6 neutrons
6 electrons

Atomic mass: 12.01

Carbon is the most flexible and "friendly" atom on the Periodic Table. It will bond with many other elements, although its favorites are hydrogen and oxygen. If there are no other atoms around to bond with, carbon will bond to itself, forming pure-carbon substances such as diamonds, graphite and coal. That's right, coal and diamonds are made of the same stuff! The most fascinating pure-carbon structure is the buckyball, a hollow sphere of 60 carbon atoms arranged in the same pattern as a soccer ball (hexagons surrounded by pentagons).

Carbon is found in the air around us as carbon dioxide, CO_2. Vehicles can put both CO_2 and CO (carbon monoxide) into the air as by-products of combustion. CO is very dangerous and many people have CO detectors in their homes if they have a furnace that burns natural gas, CH_4.

Carbon can bond to three oxygen atoms and make the carbonate ion, CO_3^{2-}. If a calcium atom sticks to carbonate, we get calcium carbonate, $CaCO_3$. Calcium carbonate is the main ingredient in the mineral calcite and in the rock known as limestone. Sea shells are a biological form of calcium carbonate.

Hydrocarbon molecules are made of just carbon and hydrogen atoms and can be small (CH_4, natural gas), medium-sized (C_8H_{18}, octane, liquid gasoline) or so long we can't even count the carbon atoms (plastics and rubbers). Carbon and hydrogen atoms can also form a ring known as benzene. The benzene ring, or an adaptation of it, is at the heart of thousands of molecules, including polystyrene plastic, Styrofoam®, food preservatives, cholesterol, natural almond flavor, spot removers, moth balls, paints, and medicines.

Many biological molecules have carbon at their core. Proteins, fats and sugars are all carbon-based substances. DNA, the extremely long ladder-shaped molecule that is like a library of information for living cells, has carbon atoms at key points in its structure. Carbon is also at center of many other molecules essential to life, including enzymes.

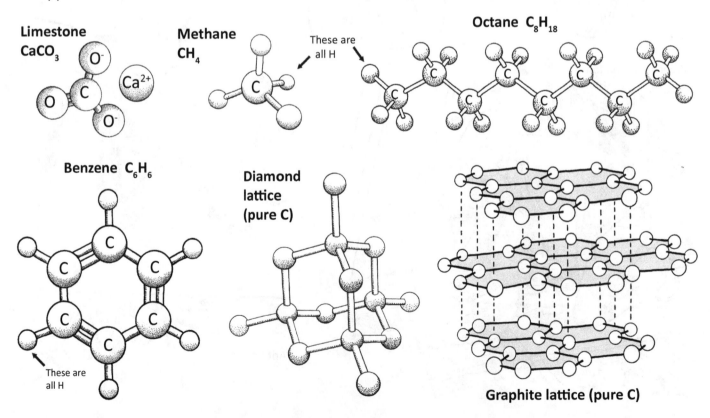

Limestone $CaCO_3$

Methane CH_4

These are all H

Octane C_8H_{18}

Benzene C_6H_6

These are all H

Diamond lattice (pure C)

Graphite lattice (pure C)

sample-12

6 Carbon C

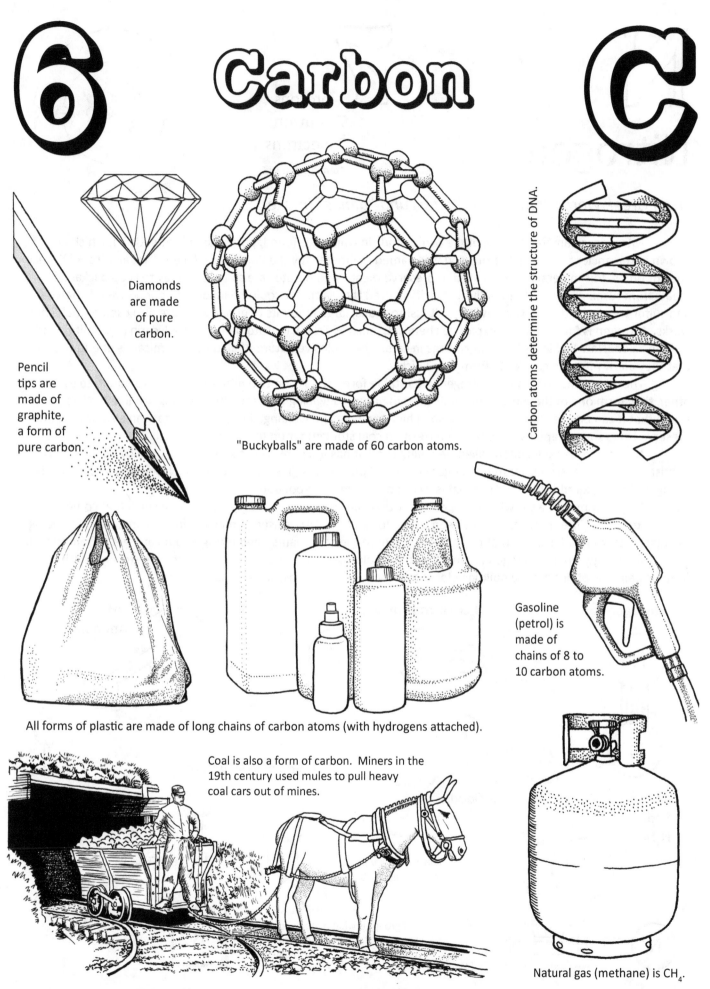

Diamonds are made of pure carbon.

Pencil tips are made of graphite, a form of pure carbon.

"Buckyballs" are made of 60 carbon atoms.

Carbon atoms determine the structure of DNA.

Gasoline (petrol) is made of chains of 8 to 10 carbon atoms.

All forms of plastic are made of long chains of carbon atoms (with hydrogens attached).

Coal is also a form of carbon. Miners in the 19th century used mules to pull heavy coal cars out of mines.

Natural gas (methane) is CH_4.

Nitrogen

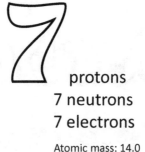

7 protons
7 neutrons
7 electrons

Atomic mass: 14.0

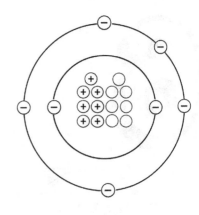

From Greek words "nitron" (saltpeter) and "genes" (make)

Nitrogen is named after one of the compounds in which it is found, potassium nitrate (KNO_3), which was known in the ancient world as "nitron" and was named "saltpeter" by the Europeans. ("Peter" means "rock.") Since ancient times, this mineral has been used to preserve meats, and nitrates are still used today to keep packaged meats from turning brown. Eventually, it was discovered that saltpeter could be made into gunpowder if charcoal and sulfur were added it to. Gunpowder isn't just for guns; large amounts of gunpowder are also used to make fireworks. Nitrogen is found in other explosive chemicals, such as TNT (trinitrotoluene), nitroglycerin (dynamite), and sodium azide (NaN_3) which is found in air bags in cars. The explosive nature of all these chemicals is due to the fact that they allow nitrogen gas, N_2, to form very quickly.

The air around us is mostly nitrogen in its stable form, N_2. When two nitrogen atoms are bound to each other, they form one of the most stable molecules in nature, unwilling to react with anything around it. N_2 is so stable that it can be used as a fireproof shield in high temperature welding. Pure nitrogen gas can also protect and preserve fruits such as apples, keeping them fresh (in cold storage) for up to two years.

N_2O is nitrous oxide, often called "laughing gas." It has a slightly sweet smell and is used by doctors and dentists as a mild anesthetic for minor surgery or dental procedures. It's easy to confuse N_2O with NO_2, but NO_2 is nitrogen dioxide, a reddish-brown gas that is a common form of air pollution.

NH_3 is ammonia, a gas with a pungent odor that can sting your nose. It's that strong smell that comes from wet diapers or cat litter boxes that have been sitting for a while. NH_3 is used in many industrial processes, including the manufacturing of fertilizers that can put nitrogen into the soil. Plants need nitrogen but can't get it from the air.

In biology, we find nitrogen in more complex molecules, such as amino acids, which are strung together to form proteins. Proteins are the building blocks from which cells and tissues are made.

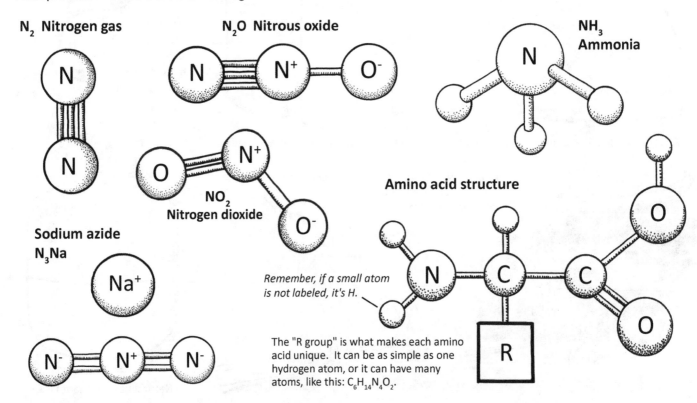

N_2 Nitrogen gas

N_2O Nitrous oxide

NH_3 Ammonia

NO_2 Nitrogen dioxide

Sodium azide
N_3Na

Amino acid structure

Remember, if a small atom is not labeled, it's H.

The "R group" is what makes each amino acid unique. It can be as simple as one hydrogen atom, or it can have many atoms, like this: $C_6H_{14}N_4O_2$.

7

N

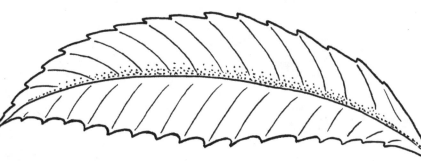

Nitrogen

If leaves don't get enough nitrogen they lose their green color.

Nitrates and nitrites are used to preserve meats.

Throughout history, horns have often been used to store gunpowder (a nitrogen compound).

Dynamite contains a nitrogen compound: nitroglycerin.

Plant fertilizers often contain nitrogen.

Some cleaning products contain ammonia, NH_3.

Air bags in vehicles are inflated with nitrogen.

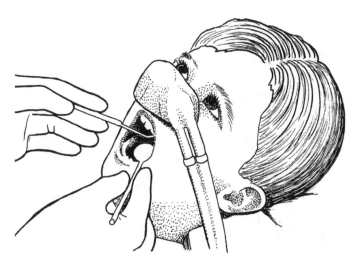

N_2O, nitrous oxide, is used by dentists as a mild anesthetic.

Oxygen

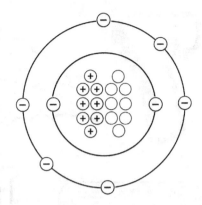

8 protons
8 neutrons
8 electrons

Atomic mass: 15.9

From Greek words "oxy" (sour) and "genes" (make)

Oxygen's name comes from the fact that when it was discovered in the late 1700s, it was mistakenly believed to be the key factor in the formation of acids, which taste sour (lemon juice, for example). This idea was eventually proven wrong, but by that time the name "oxygen" was being used by everyone and it was too late to change it.

Oxygen is the third most abundant element in the universe, after hydrogen and helium. Oxygen is in the air all around us as O_2. Nitrogen, N_2, makes up about 78% of our atmosphere and oxygen comes in second at about 20%. In the upper atmosphere we find three oxygen atoms stuck together to form ozone, O_3. Ozone layers help to protect earth from dangerous ultra-violet radiation produced by the sun.

Oxygen is a very reactive element and will bond to most of the other elements to form compounds whose names usually end in "ate," "ide," or "ite." The most well known oxide compound is water, H_2O. A similar molecule is H_2O_2, hydrogen peroxide, whose usefulness as a disinfectant is due to the fact that the second oxygen atom falls off easily, reverting back to H_2O. A single oxygen atom is very dangerous and will try to steal electrons from any atom or molecule it comes into contact with. We have body cells that use single oxygens as "bullets" to fire at germs.

All forms of animal life need oxygen for cellular respiration, the process by which cells extract energy from sugars and fats. Fish and other sea life use oxygen that is dissolved into the water around them. Plants produce oxygen as a waste product of photosynthesis, so there is a balance between oxygen produced and oxygen used.

Plants use carbon dioxide, CO_2, from the air to make sugar molecules (glucose, $C_6H_{12}O_6$).

Oxygen is found in the crust of the earth bound to the element silicon to form minerals such as quartz, feldspar, mica, and olivine. All these minerals are based on the silicon tetrahedron, SiO_4, which forms crystal lattices.

When oxygen is cooled down to -183° C it becomes a liquid. Oxygen is often transported in its liquid state because it takes up less space. One liter of liquid oxygen expands to become 840 liters of oxygen gas. Oxygen gas is used in medical devices, in steel production, in plastic manufacturing and as fuel in welding. Liquid oxygen is used (along with liquid hydrogen) as rocket fuel.

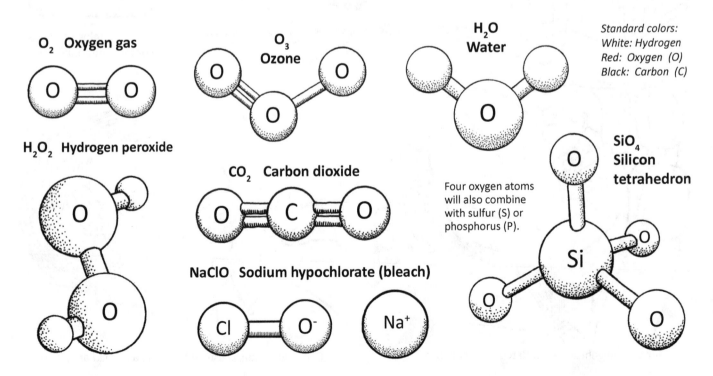

O_2 **Oxygen gas**

O_3
Ozone

H_2O
Water

Standard colors:
White: Hydrogen
Red: Oxygen (O)
Black: Carbon (C)

H_2O_2 **Hydrogen peroxide**

CO_2 **Carbon dioxide**

SiO_4
Silicon tetrahedron

Four oxygen atoms will also combine with sulfur (S) or phosphorus (P).

NaClO **Sodium hypochlorate (bleach)**

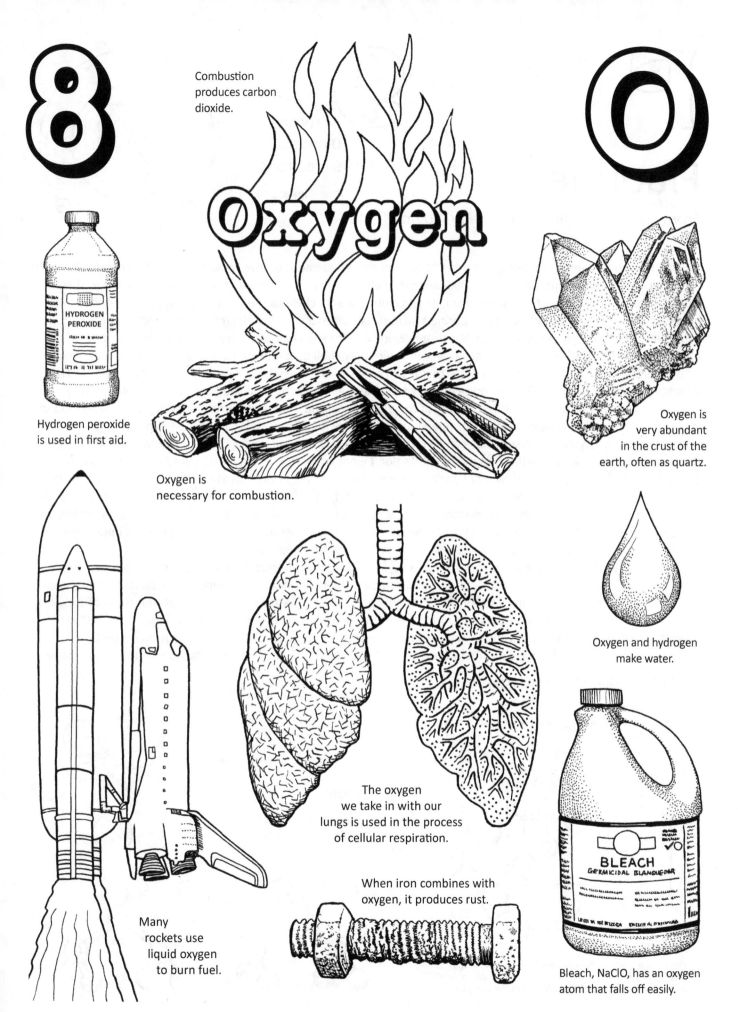

8

Combustion produces carbon dioxide.

Oxygen

O

Hydrogen peroxide is used in first aid.

Oxygen is necessary for combustion.

Oxygen is very abundant in the crust of the earth, often as quartz.

Oxygen and hydrogen make water.

The oxygen we take in with our lungs is used in the process of cellular respiration.

Many rockets use liquid oxygen to burn fuel.

When iron combines with oxygen, it produces rust.

Bleach, NaClO, has an oxygen atom that falls off easily.

Fluorine

From Latin word "fluere" meaning "to flow"

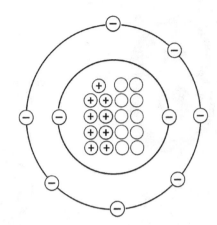

9 protons
10 neutrons
9 electrons

Atomic mass: 18.9

Fluorine is famous for being the most "electronegative" element on the Periodic Table. This means that it can hold on to other atoms more tightly than any other element can. This is due to its size and its number of electrons. Because fluorine is a fairly small atom, its electrons are very close to the positively charged protons in the nucleus. Opposite charges attract, and fluorine's protons are able to hold the electrons very tightly. (Larger atoms can lose some of their outer electrons.) Because fluorine's outer shell has only 7 electrons, it falls one short of the perfect number: 8. Atoms with one empty place in their outer shell desperately want to steal or borrow an electron to fill that slot. Fluorine is so desperate that it will grab the first available electron it finds, usually an electron belonging to another atom. Thus, fluorine is never found alone in nature. (A single F atom is very dangerous!)

Fluorine is often found in the company of the element calcium, forming calcium fluoride, CaF_2. When found in rocks, CaF_2 is a mineral called fluorite (or fluorspar). Very pure fluorite crystals can be made into camera and telescope lenses. Crystals of lesser value can be crushed into a powder and used as "flux" in metal smelting. The fluorine atoms will grab impurities that metallurgists don't want in the hot, liquid metal. Getting rid of these contaminants makes the hot metal flow more easily. Fluorine's name comes from this ability to make liquid metals flow.

When fluorine grabs a hydrogen atom, hydrofluoric acid, HF, is formed. This acid is very dangerous to work with. It burns flesh and it steals calcium from bones. It is used to etch designs into glass because it is one of the few substances that can dissolve glass. Despite the fact that it is so dangerous, fluorine does play an important role in the body, being one of the minerals that help to make our teeth very strong.

Sulfur atoms can bond to six fluorines, making SF_6, sulfur hexafluoride. Unlike HF, this substance is very safe. SF_6 is a gas that won't react with anything and can be used as insulation. A similar molecule is uranium hexafluoride, UF_6. This molecule is used to "enrich" uranium by collecting U atoms that have an atomic mass of 235.

When fluorine bonds with carbon, it forms C_2F_4, tetra-fluoro-ethylene, better known as Teflon®. Teflon® is very slippery so when pans are coated with it, they become "non-stick." A similar substance is poly-tetra-fluoro-ethylene, better known by the brand name Gore-Tex®. Gore-Tex® fabric is rainproof while still allowing body moisture to escape.

CaF_2 Calcium fluorite (crystal lattice)

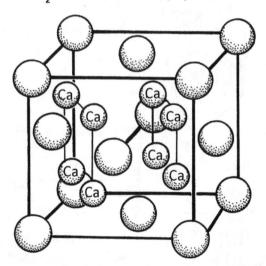

This cube is called a unit cell. We see only part of the crystal, so it seems like the math is wrong. If you looked at the entire crystal, there would be 2 Fs for every Ca.

SF_6 Sulfur hexafluoride

The central atom is sulfur. Artists usually make sulfur yellow. All the other atoms are fluorine.

C_2F_4 Teflon®

This molecule is a very long polymer made of thousands of carbon atoms bonded to fluorine atoms.

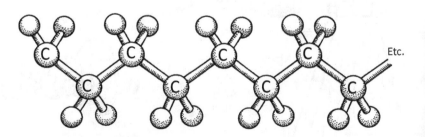

Etc.

9 F

Fluorine

Fluoride is often found in toothpaste because it helps to prevent cavities.

Fluorite crystals are often green or purple.

Hydrofluoric acid, HF, is dangerous!

Hydrofluoric Acid

Fluorite is used for high magnification camera lenses.

Gore-Tex® clothes use a modified form of Teflon®.

Teflon® tape for plumbing

Teflon® makes cooking pans "non-stick."

Fluorine is used as a "flux" in the smelting of metal. Smelting means heating mineral ores until they become a liquid (often bright yellow in color). Metals can then be collected and cooled.

Someone during Roman times carved this vase from a piece of calcium fluoride. It has stripes of dark green, dark red, and yellow-tan.

Ne

10 protons
10 neutrons
10 electrons

Atomic mass: 20.2

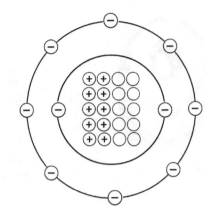

Neon

From the Greek word for "new"

Neon belongs to the family of elements called the noble gases. They are found in the last column on the right side of the Periodic Table. The noble gases are very lucky because their outer electron shells are completely filled. They do not have any empty slots, nor do they have any extra electrons to give away. This is why they will not interact with other atoms. The noble gases are called "inert" because they are so nonreactive. Neon is sometimes called the most inert element on the Periodic Table.

Like most of the noble gases, neon can be safely used in places where there is electricity, such as inside fluorescent light tubes. Neon lights (the ones that actually have neon in them) glow with an orange-red color. Most of the lights that are called "neon" lights are actually filled with other gases and with powdered minerals that produce colors like green, yellow, or blue.

Neon is used in cold-cathode voltage regulator tubes, which look a lot like old-fashioned vacuum tubes. A similar product, called "nixie tubes," are used to make an unusual type of digital clock. Neon can also be used in high-voltage indicator devices, and in structures that absorb lightning strikes. Helium, another noble gas, is used with neon to make helium-neon (HeNe) lasers, which produce a bright red line of light.

Neon is found in the air all around us, but in very small quantities. The way you collect it out of the air is to chill the air to hundreds of degrees below zero, until all the gases turn to liquid. Then the temperature is turned up very slowly, one degree at a time. At -246° C, liquid neon turns back into a gas and is captured.

Neon was discovered at about the same time as the elements krypton and xenon, in 1898, by Sir William Ramsay and his assistant Morris Travers, using this chilling technique. As they watched the gases appear, some of them were familiar, such as oxygen, nitrogen, helium, and carbon dioxide. Then they found a "new" one, so they named it neon, after the Greek word for new.

Sir William Ramsay in his lab

Neon does not form molecules

Ne   Ne

Ne   Ne

Ne

Ne

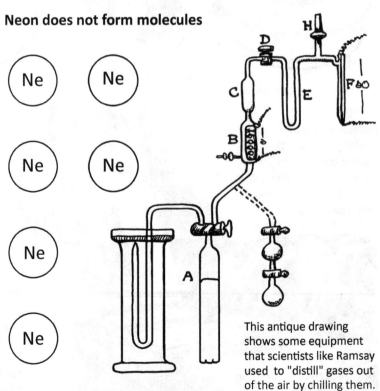

This antique drawing shows some equipment that scientists like Ramsay used to "distill" gases out of the air by chilling them.

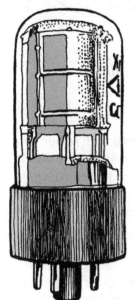

This is a cold-cathode voltage regulator tube. They are used only rarely now, as solid state regulators have mostly replaced them.

Café

OPEN

CLOSED

Neon signs (that actually have neon in them) glow bright orange-red.

This is a "nixie" tube. It contains tiny neon tubes shaped like numbers. The tubes can be used to make clocks that are purchased by collectors as novelties.

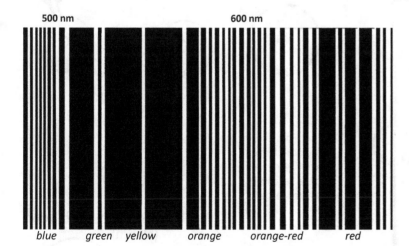

500 nm   600 nm

blue   green   yellow   orange   orange-red   red

If you look at glowing neon gas through a spectrometer, this is what you will see. The small amount of blue and green light that comes from glowing neon atoms is drowned out by all the orange and red.

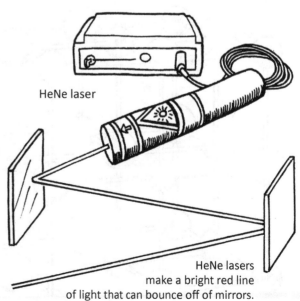

HeNe laser

HeNe lasers make a bright red line of light that can bounce off of mirrors.

 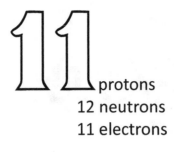 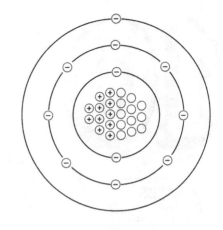

Na 11
protons
12 neutrons
11 electrons

Sodium

Atomic mass: 22.9

The name comes from the substance in which it was discovered, "caustic soda."

The symbol, Na, is from the Latin "natrium," meaning "sodium carbonate."

Sodium was discovered by the famous chemist Sir Humphry Davy, in 1807. He discovered both sodium and potassium in that year, using electricity to pull the atoms out of a solution. The solution he used for sodium was called caustic soda (known to us today as sodium hydroxide, NaOH), and it is from that substance that sodium gets its name. Pure sodium is a very soft, shiny silver metal that quickly turns dark gray if it is exposed to air. Putting sodium into water causes it to burst into bright yellow flames, so chemists keep their samples of sodium in jars of oil, protected from both water and air.

Sodium has only one electron in its outer shell, making it desperate to get rid of that lonely electron, even though getting rid of it will mean upsetting the equal balance of electrons and protons. It prefers having a positive electrical charge to having a lonely electron in an orbit all by itself. After a sodium atom loses that outer electron, it is called an "ion" instead of an atom. An ion is an atom that does not have an equal number of electrons and protons.

Sodium is always found attached to other atoms, and one of its favorites is chlorine, making a molecule of NaCl (sodium chloride). NaCl forms crystals that we know as table salt. Salt has a long history of being useful in many food preparation processes, including preserving meats so they do not spoil.

Sodium lights were used widely in public areas before the invention of LED lights because the bulbs had a very long life. Sodium bulbs give off a very yellow glow, which comes from sodium's spectral lines.

Sodium plays important roles in the body. In the blood, it helps to maintain proper blood pressure; it flows in and out of nerve cells, allowing them to transmit electrical signals.

NaCl Sodium chloride (table salt) crystal lattice

(The atoms that are not marked are chlorine, Cl.)

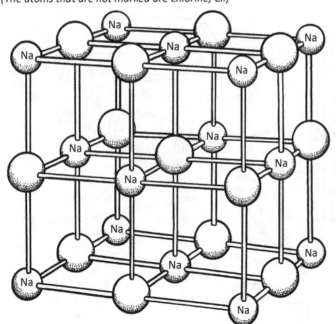

NaHCO₃ Sodium bicarbonate
(baking soda)

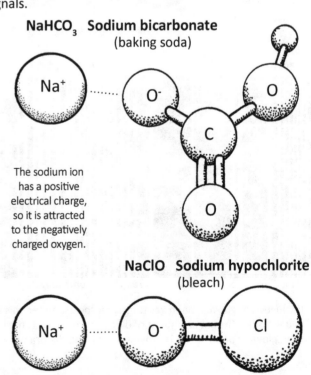

The sodium ion has a positive electrical charge, so it is attracted to the negatively charged oxygen.

NaClO Sodium hypochlorite
(bleach)

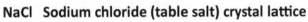

11

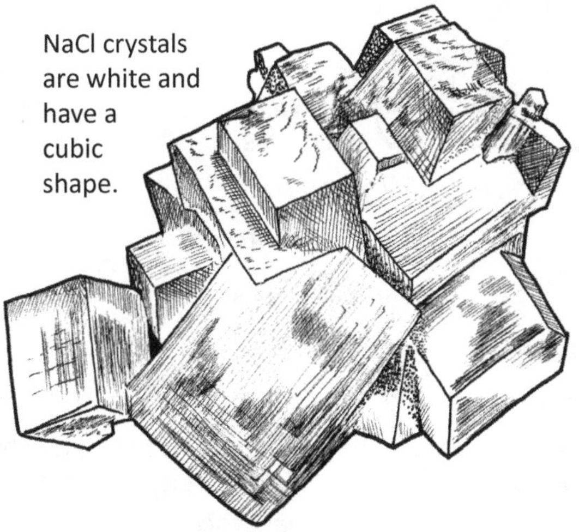

NaCl crystals are white and have a cubic shape.

Na

Sodium

Table salt is NaCl.

BAKING SODA

Baking soda makes things rise in the oven. Its formula is $NaHCO_3$.

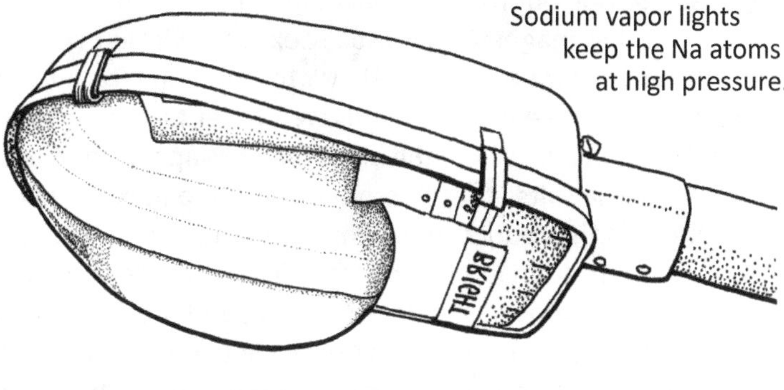

Sodium vapor lights keep the Na atoms at high pressure.

Bleach and Borax both contain sodium.

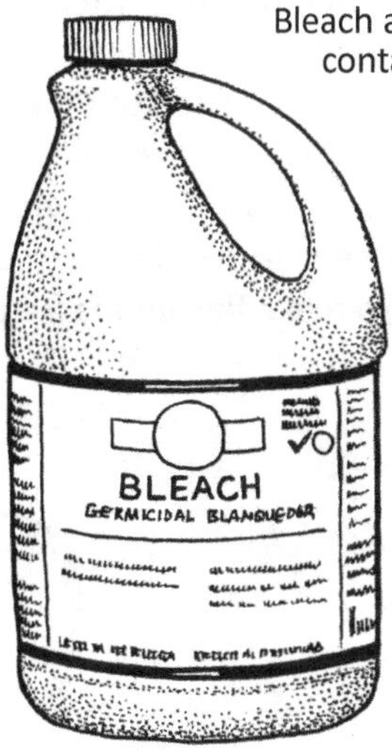

BLEACH GERMICIDAL BLANDUEDER

BORAX DETERGENT BOOSTER

The sodium-potassium pump is found in cell membranes.

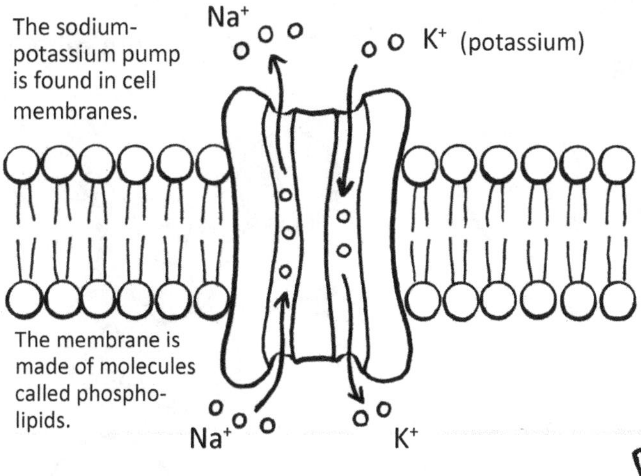

Na^+

K^+ (potassium)

The membrane is made of molecules called phospholipids.

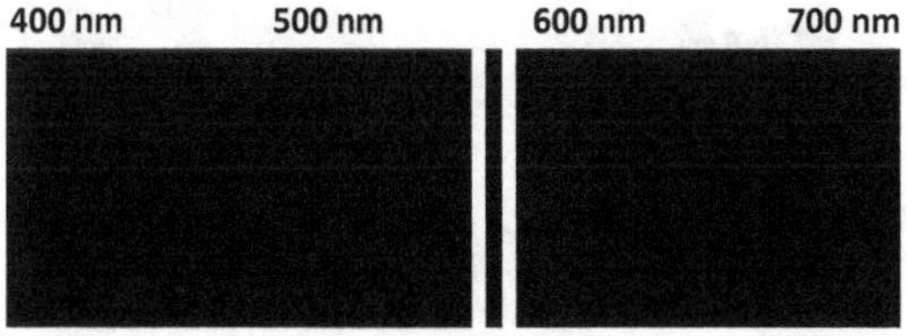

Na^+ K^+

This is not an air tank. It is a "re-breather." It recycles air, using NaOH and CaO to remove CO_2.

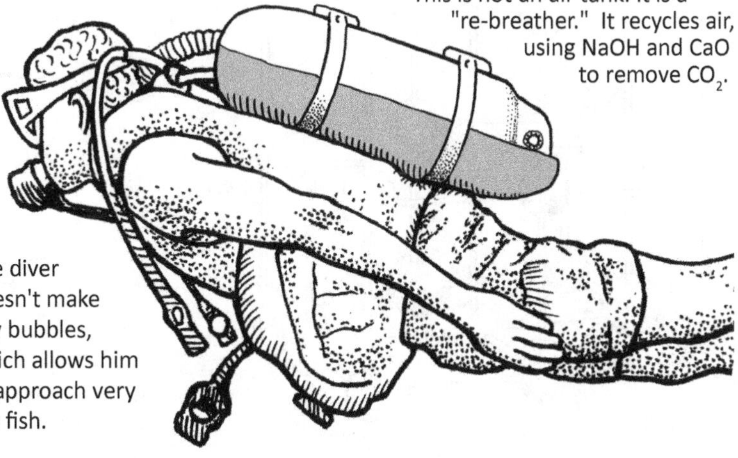

400 nm	500 nm	600 nm	700 nm

yellow

Sodium has a very distinct emission spectrum. Burning sodium produces just two yellow lines.

The diver doesn't make any bubbles, which allows him to approach very shy fish.

 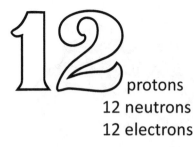

12 protons
12 neutrons
12 electrons

Atomic mass: 24.3

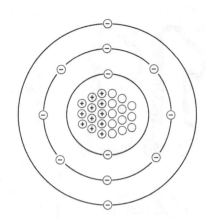

Magnesium

From the area of Greece called Magnesia

Magnesium was discovered and named in 1808 by Sir Humphry Davy. He used electricity to pull magnesium atoms out of a chemical solution. This technique, called electrolysis, was used by Robert Bunsen in 1852 to produce enough magnesium that it could be evaluated for use in many industrial processes. Magnesium was found to be light and strong but melted at low temperatures. It is most useful when combined with aluminum to make an alloy.

Today, magnesium is usually extracted from ocean water, which has almost as much magnesium as it does sodium and chlorine (NaCl, salt). Water from underground sources can also contain magnesium, as John Epsom discovered in the early 1600s. His well water tasted bitter but it turned out have wonderful healing properties, especially for skin. When the bitter water evaporated, it left behind crystals that are known today as Epsom salts, $MgSO_4$. These salts are still commonly used to make soaking baths as a remedy for unhealthy skin or sore muscles. Another health product containing magnesium is "milk of magnesia," $Mg(OH)_2$, which is used as an antacid.

Magnesium is very abundant in the Earth's crust, particularly in a mineral called dolomite, which is very similar to limestone. Limestone is $CaCO_3$, and dolomite is $MgCO_3$. Magnesium can easily replace calcium because of the fact that both of these elements have two electrons in their outer shell. The number of electrons in the outer shell is what gives elements their ability to bond with certain atoms or molecules. Magnesium also likes to bond to oxygen to make MgO, magnesium oxide, a mineral commonly found in rocks.

Metals that contain magnesium are used to make parts for many machines and devices, including airplanes, rockets, cars, sports equipment, and electronic devices.

Magnesium burns with a brilliant white light, which makes it ideal for use in fireworks, sparklers, flares, and tracer bullets. (Tracer bullets produce a flash of light so you can see them as they speed through the air.) Before the age of LEDs, magnesium was used to make flashbulbs for cameras.

MgO Magnesium oxide
MgS Magnesium sulfide

Both MgO and MgS will form lattices.
(The smaller balls represent Mg atoms.)

MgCO₃ Dolomite

MgSO₄ Magnesium sulfate
(Epsom salt)

What element
is magnesium
attracted to
in all of these
molecules?

Mg(OH)₂ Magnesium hydroxide
This substance can also form a lattice, but much
more complicated than MgO or MgS.

*Hydrogen is often
unlabeled.*

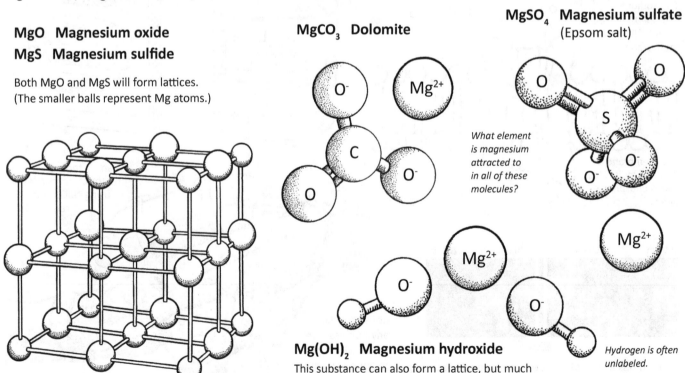

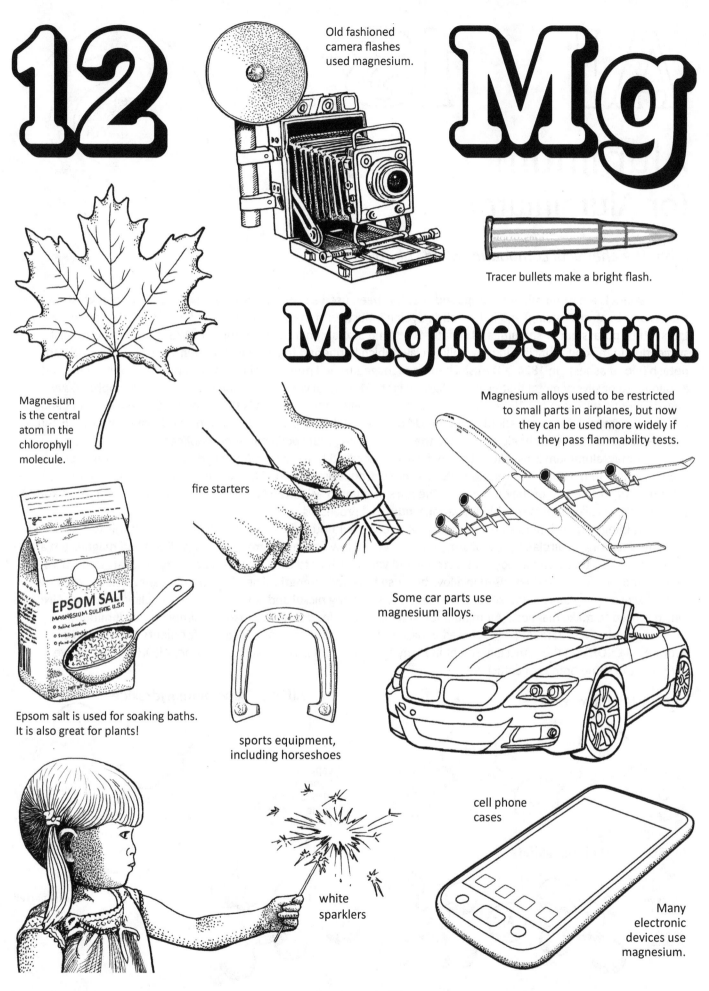

12

Mg

Magnesium

Old fashioned camera flashes used magnesium.

Tracer bullets make a bright flash.

Magnesium is the central atom in the chlorophyll molecule.

fire starters

Magnesium alloys used to be restricted to small parts in airplanes, but now they can be used more widely if they pass flammability tests.

EPSOM SALT
MAGNESIUM SULFATE U.S.P.

Epsom salt is used for soaking baths. It is also great for plants!

sports equipment, including horseshoes

Some car parts use magnesium alloys.

cell phone cases

white sparklers

Many electronic devices use magnesium.

Al

Aluminum
(or Aluminium)

13
protons
14 neutrons
13 electrons

Atomic mass: 26.9

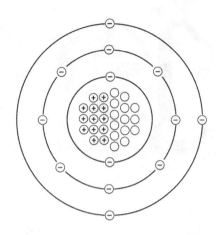

From the chemical compound called "alum"

Alum is a natural mineral compound that has been used since ancient times by doctors (to quickly shrink tissues and to stop bleeding) and in the fabric dyeing industry. In the 1700s, chemists figured out that alum contains either potassium or sodium, and sulfate, SO_4^{2-}, and also an unknown element. In 1754, a German chemist succeeded in making artificial alum by boiling clay (which happened to contain aluminum) with sulfuric acid and potash (wood ashes). In 1824, a Danish chemist managed to pull pure aluminum atoms out of a solution to produce a solid lump of silvery metal that was very lightweight. The metal was not officially named until Humphry Davy began working with it in the 1800s. He chose the name "aluminum," which is the name that is now used in Canada and the U.S. Years later, some scientists in the UK decided that they preferred "aluminium" because it ends in "-ium" like the names of many other elements, and they began using that spelling in their publications.

Today, aluminum is usually extracted from a rock called bauxite *(box-ite)* by grinding the rock into a powder, then making it into a hot liquid solution into which electrodes are placed. The aluminum atoms come out of the solution and stick to one of the electrodes. The pure aluminum will often have small amounts of other metals added to it to make an alloy that is suitable for various industrial processes.

Adding magnesium to aluminum makes it stronger without adding extra weight, so this alloy is widely used in the manufacturing of airplanes, boats, army tanks, and window frames. Sometimes both silicon and magnesium are added to make a three-metal alloy that is strong and very resistant to corrosion—great for making cars and trucks. Copper and zinc are also widely used in alloys because they add strength. The element manganese makes an alloy that is excellent for cooking utensils and beverage cans. Adding nickel and cobalt will make an alloy known as AlNiCo, which is used to make magnets. Aluminum foil and aluminum food trays are made of almost pure aluminum.

Aluminum sulfate, $Al_2(SO_4)_3$, is used in paper manufacturing and as a fertilizer for plants. Aluminum chlorohydrate, $Al_2Cl(OH)_5$, is the active ingredient in many antiperspirants. Aluminum hydroxide, $Al(OH)_3$, is the active ingredient in some brands of antacids.

Al_2O_3 Aluminum oxide

$Al(OH)_3$ Aluminum hydroxide

All of these molecules are capable of bonding with others of the same type to form mineral crystals.

$Al_2(SO_4)_3$ Aluminum sulfate

Unmarked atoms are oxygens.

Oxygen is usually colored red.

The unmarked atoms are hydrogens.

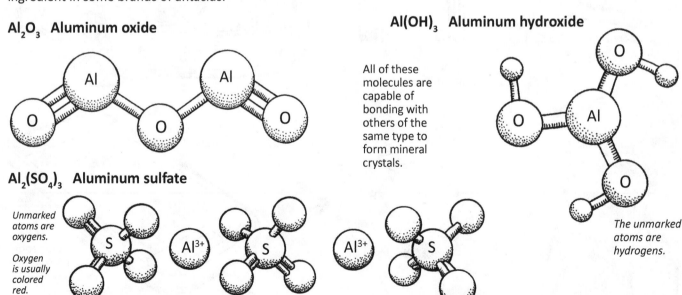

13

Rubies are a red variation of the mineral corundum, Al_2O_3.

Sapphires are also corundum, but are blue.

Al

Aluminum

Airplanes are made of aluminum alloys.

Aluminum foil is made of almost pure aluminum.

TOP BRAND FOIL

62.5

an aluminum beverage can

Alnico magnets are made of aluminum, nickel, and cobalt.

Special

ANTIPERSPIRANT

Many antiperspirants contain aluminum.

Aluminum is fairly easy to recycle.

Lightweight bicycle frames are often made of Al.

Bauxite is the main ore rock from which aluminum is extracted.

recyclable food pans and trays

Si 14

protons
14 neutrons
14 electrons

Atomic mass: 28.08

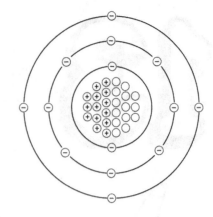

Silicon

From "silex," the Latin word for flint

Silicon was observed for the first time in 1824 by Swedish chemist Jöns Berzelius by heating a compound that contained fluorine, potassium, and silicon. Previous chemists had suspected that silicon might be an element but they were never able to get it separated from the oxygen atoms it was attached to. Pure silicon (not attached to any other atoms) is a dark blue-gray, with a very shiny surface. It is not surprising that pure silicon is shiny because silicon combines with oxygen to make glass, SiO_2.

Silicon and oxygen are the basis for the large family of silicate minerals. Silicate gemstones include agate, amethyst, flint, jasper, carnelian, calcedony, onyx, and opal. Silicate minerals that are not gemstones include olivine, hornblende, asbestos, mica (biotite and muscovite), and feldspar. Granite is a rock that is made of mixtures of quartz, feldspar and mica. Sand that is light in color is usually made of very tiny pieces of quartz and feldspar.

Quartz is an extremely useful mineral because its crystal structure produces electricity when it is squeezed. Quartz crystals can be used to make clocks, sonar devices, and ultrasound machines.

Pure silicon can be grown into crystals that become very useful when they have small amounts of boron, germanium and arsenic added to them. The crystals are used to make solid-state electronic parts such as micro-chips and transistors, which are found in devices such as computers, tablets, and cell phones.

Another way silicon can combine with oxygen is in long chains, with other small molecules attached. These long chains are called polymers and the substances they make are called silicones. Silicone substances you may be familiar with are Silly Putty®, silicone baking trays, and silicone caulk (used around windows, sinks and tubs).

A few forms of life use silicon to make their shells. Diatoms and radiolarians are beautiful microscopic pro-tozoans with shells made of SiO_2 (glass). One type of sea sponge, the glass sponge, uses silicon to build its skeleton.

SiC Silicon carbide

These silicon-carbon units stack together to form the lattice shape shown below.

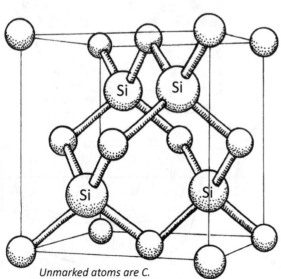

Unmarked atoms are C.

SiCl₄ Silicon tetrachloride

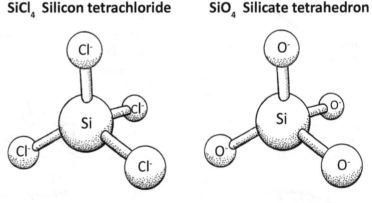

These tetrahedral molecules usually bond with many others identical to themselves to form some kind of lattice shape.

SiO₄ Silicate tetrahedron

Silicone polymers (There are many options for what R can be.)

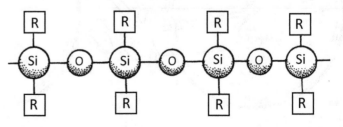

14 Silicon Si

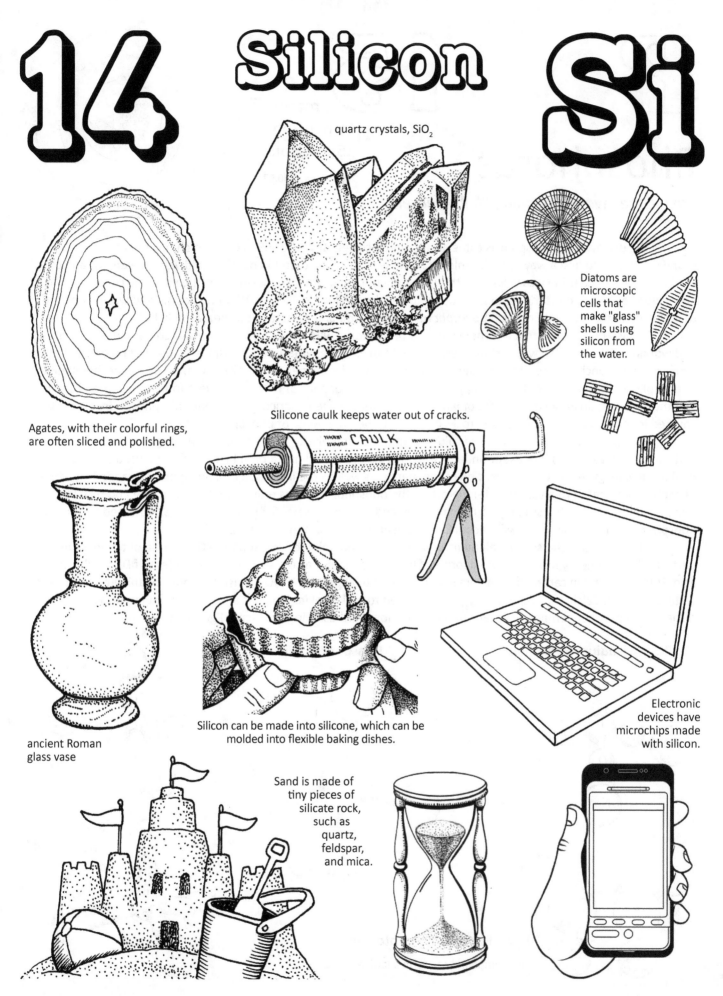

quartz crystals, SiO_2

Diatoms are microscopic cells that make "glass" shells using silicon from the water.

Agates, with their colorful rings, are often sliced and polished.

Silicone caulk keeps water out of cracks.

CAULK

ancient Roman glass vase

Silicon can be made into silicone, which can be molded into flexible baking dishes.

Electronic devices have microchips made with silicon.

Sand is made of tiny pieces of silicate rock, such as quartz, feldspar, and mica.

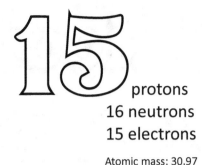
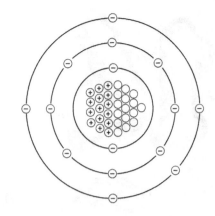

15 protons
16 neutrons
15 electrons

Atomic mass: 30.97

Phosphorus

From Greek words meaning "light-bearer"

The discovery of phosphorus came about quite accidentally. In 1669, a German chemist named Hennig Brand was trying to find a way to make gold. (Chemists at this time didn't know that gold was an element and could not be made.) Since urine was yellow, he thought it might contain very small amounts of gold, so he collected gallons and gallons of urine and starting boiling it down to get the "yellow stuff" out. What he got instead was white stuff that glowed in the dark. He named it *phosphorus mirabilis*, meaning "miraculous bearer of light."

It wasn't until 1769 that another source of phosphorus was discovered. Bones also contained phosphorus, and working with bone ash was certainly less smelly than working with urine. Phosphorus was not recognized as an element until French chemist Antoine Lavoisier began experimenting with it in 1777. In the 1840s, another source of phosphorus was discovered: bird droppings (guano). Vast supplies of bird guano were found on tropical islands and they became an important source of plant fertilizer for European agriculture. Eventually, phosphorus was discovered in rocks in the late 1800s, and rocks continue to be our source of phosphorus today.

Pure phosphorus comes in three colors: white, red, and black. White is the most dangerous to work with and can burst into flames if not kept under water. It is also toxic and had a brief history of being used as a poison. Its flammability gave rise to the invention of the match, as well as the invention of new types of weapons. If white phosphorus is heated to a very high temperature, the phosphorus atoms rearrange their structure and turn red. Red phosphorus is much less dangerous than white, and was much safer for making matches. If heated further, red phosphorus will turn black and will become very safe and stable, but much less useful.

Phosphorus is an essential element to both plants and animals. Phosphate, PO_4^{3-}, is one of the working parts in ATP, the energy molecule for all forms of life. Phosphate is also a structural component of DNA. Phosphoric acid, H_3PO_4 is found in carbonated beverages. Trisodium phosphate, Na_3PO_4, is used in some cleaning products and water softeners. Calcium phosphate, $Ca_3(PO_4)_2$, is used to make baking powder and in the manufacturing of china dishes. Various other compounds that contain phosphorus are used in fluorescent light bulbs.

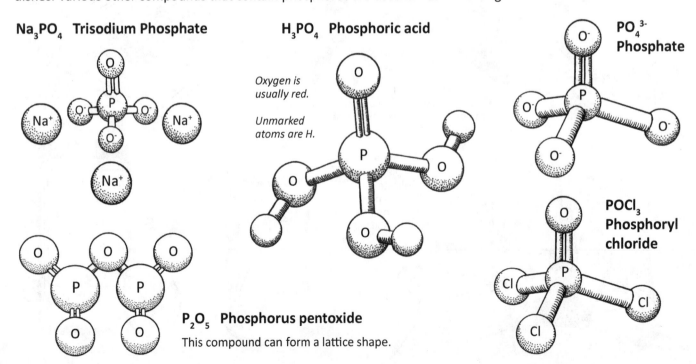

Na_3PO_4 **Trisodium Phosphate**

H_3PO_4 **Phosphoric acid**

Oxygen is usually red.

Unmarked atoms are H.

PO_4^{3-} **Phosphate**

$POCl_3$ **Phosphoryl chloride**

P_2O_5 **Phosphorus pentoxide**

This compound can form a lattice shape.

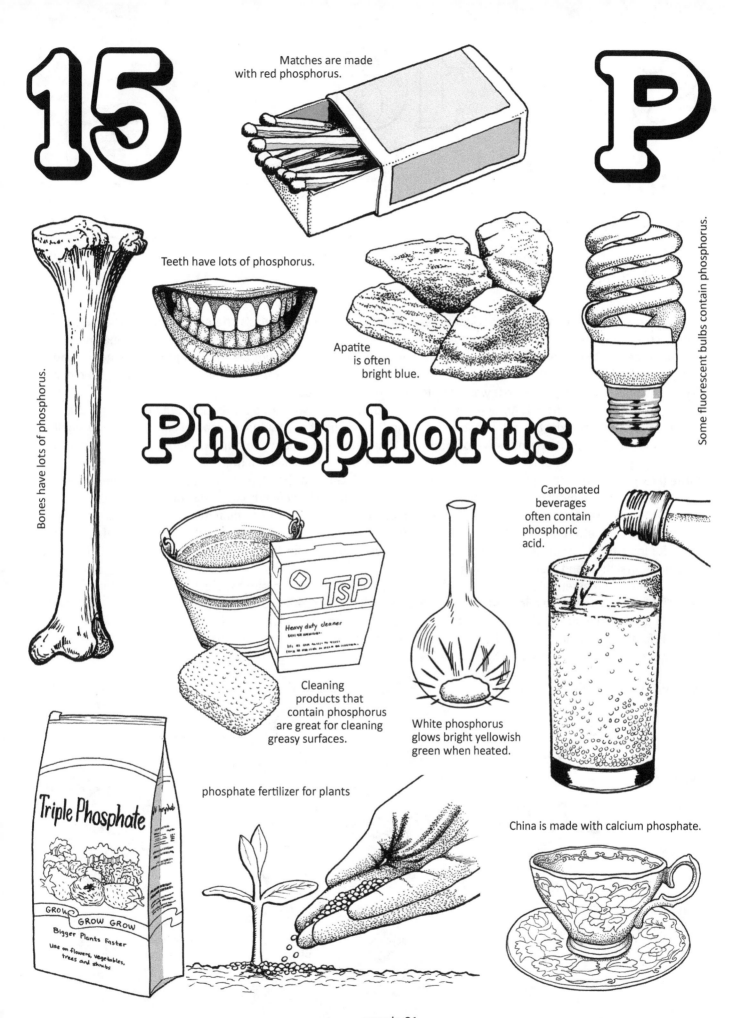

15

P

Matches are made with red phosphorus.

Teeth have lots of phosphorus.

Apatite is often bright blue.

Some fluorescent bulbs contain phosphorus.

Bones have lots of phosphorus.

Phosphorus

Carbonated beverages often contain phosphoric acid.

TSP
Heavy duty cleaner

Cleaning products that contain phosphorus are great for cleaning greasy surfaces.

White phosphorus glows bright yellowish green when heated.

phosphate fertilizer for plants

China is made with calcium phosphate.

Triple Phosphate

GROW GROW GROW
Bigger Plants Faster
Use on flowers, vegetables, trees and shrubs

S 16 protons
16 neutrons
16 electrons

Atomic mass: 32.06

Sulfur
(or Sulphur)

From the Latin "sulphurium"

People knew about sulfur in ancient times, but they did not know it was a chemical element. They used sulfur in some of the same ways we use it today. In the Middle East, sulfur was used as a topical medicine and as an insecticide. In China, they discovered it was not only useful in medicine but also as an ingredient in gunpowder. Sulfur was also known and used in India and Greece. The historical name for it translates as "brimstone," meaning "burning stone," probably because it was often found around volcanoes.

In 1777, French chemist Antoine Lavoisier realized that sulfur was not a compound, but an element. Sulfur is an element that can exist by itself in nature. You can find lumps of pure sulfur, which are pale yellow and smell like a lit match. Though it doesn't need to bond with other atoms, it is happy to bond with many different atoms, becoming a part of lots of different compounds. In geology, sulfur is an ingredient in these minerals: galena (PbS), pyrite (FeS_2), barite ($BaSO_4$), gypsum ($CaSO_4$), sphalerite (ZnS), cinnabar (HgS), and stibnite (Sb_2S_3). Some of these minerals are useful in industry, such as gypsum, which is used to make plasterboard walls for houses.

Most of the sulfur used in industry today comes from petroleum, rather than minerals. Sulfur is a natural by-product when petroleum is refined (made into a usable product like gasoline and oils). The most useful form of sulfur for industry is sulfuric acid, H_2SO_4. Sulfuric acid is used to make fertilizer, lead-acid batteries, insecticides and fungicides, matches, and many other things.

Sulfur is an essential ingredient for all of life and is found in many organic molecules. Sulfur compounds called "thiols" have a strong odor and are found in smelly things like garlic, rotten eggs, and skunk spray. Sulfur is found in three amino acids. The sulfur-containing amino acids form cross links, making tough proteins like keratin, which is found in skin, hair, and feathers. Sulfur cross-linking is also the key to making "vulcanized" rubber, a form of rubber tough enough to be used for vehicle tires.

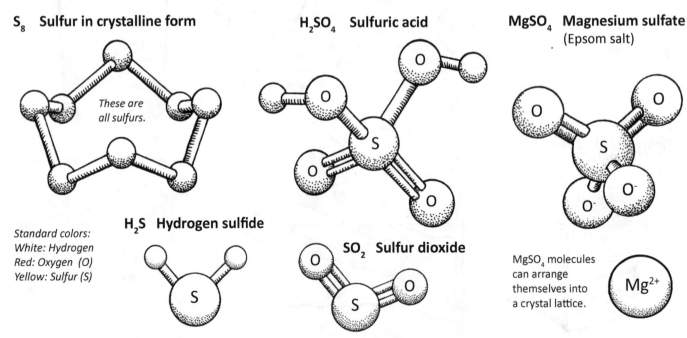

S_8 **Sulfur in crystalline form**

These are all sulfurs.

H_2SO_4 **Sulfuric acid**

MgSO$_4$ Magnesium sulfate
(Epsom salt)

Standard colors:
White: Hydrogen
Red: Oxygen (O)
Yellow: Sulfur (S)

H_2S **Hydrogen sulfide**

SO_2 **Sulfur dioxide**

MgSO$_4$ molecules can arrange themselves into a crystal lattice.

Mg^{2+}

16

Volcanoes can put SO_2 and H_2S into the air.

S

Iron pyrite, FeS_2 ("fool's gold") forms shiny gold cubic crystals.

Sulfur

Barite, $BaSO_4$, often forms in this shape, called a desert rose.

Jupiter's moon, Io, is yellow and orange, due to the large amount of sulfur produced by its many volcanoes.

Sulfur is used to make "vulcanized" rubber for tires.

Car batteries use sulfuric acid.

You can smell the sulfur in burning matches.

Sulfur compounds are found in many smelly things, including skunk spray and garlic.

Epsom salt $MgSO_4$

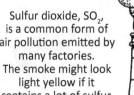

Sulfur dioxide, SO_2, is a common form of air pollution emitted by many factories. The smoke might look light yellow if it contains a lot of sulfur.

Cl

17

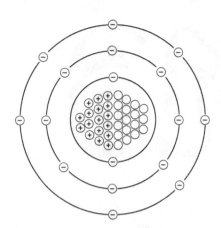

protons
18 neutrons
17 electrons

Atomic mass: 35.45

Chlorine

From Greek word "chloros" meaning "light green"

Chlorine is very reactive and is capable of bonding with almost any element on the Periodic Table. It is a member of the halogen family (the "salt makers") along with fluorine, bromine, and iodine. All these elements are very reactive, due to the fact that they have 7 electrons in their outer shells, one short of having the full number, 8. When they bond with elements in the first two columns of the Periodic Table, they form salts. Chlorine will form many salts, including NaCl, KCl, RbCl, $MgCl_2$, $CaCl_2$, and $SrCl_2$.

In its pure form, chlorine is a greenish gas. Several chemists discovered chlorine gas, but did not know what it was. Humphry Davy was the first to realize it was a new element and in 1810 he named it "chlorine."

The most common compound that contains chlorine is NaCl, table salt. Chlorine is one of the essential elements that all living things need, and it plays many roles in the human body. Our stomachs produce HCl, hydrochloric acid, to digest proteins. One of our immune cells uses a chlorine compound to poison and kill germs.

In the early 1800s, chemists discovered chlorine's ability to disinfect, even though germs had not yet been discovered. Chlorine compounds began to be used to clean surfaces and equipment in hospitals. Soon after, they found that it could be added to drinking water to prevent illnesses such as cholera. Today, we still use chlorine-based bleaches, such as sodium hypochlorite, NaClO, to disinfect, and we still add chlorine to drinking water. Public swimming pools are often treated with chlorine to keep them germ-free.

Chlorine is used in thousands of industrial processes, either as a reactant or as part of the final product. It is used in the manufacturing of paper, plastics, medicines, insecticides, textiles, dyes, paints, and solvents. Carbon tetrachloride, CCl_4, is used in dry cleaning. White PVC pipes are made of polyvinyl chloride.

Sadly, chlorine has also been used as a weapon. In World War I, chlorine gas was used in smoke bombs. The gas would go into the lungs and turn into hydrochloric acid, instantly destroying lung tissue.

HCl Hydrogen chloride
(also known as hydrochloric acid)

CHCl₃ Chloroform

NaCl Sodium chloride
Color the larger balls green for chlorine.
Color the smaller balls yellow for sodium.

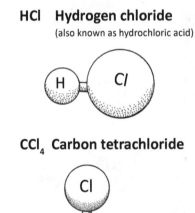

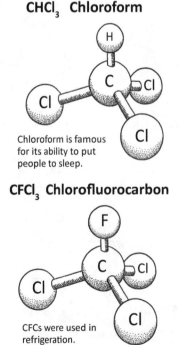

Chloroform is famous for its ability to put people to sleep.

CCl₄ Carbon tetrachloride

This compound is used in dry cleaning.

CFCl₃ Chlorofluorocarbon

CFCs were used in refrigeration.

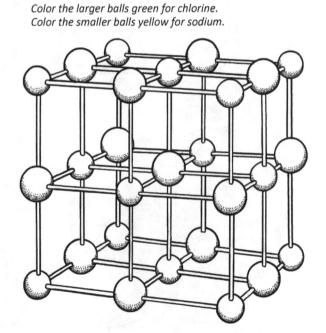

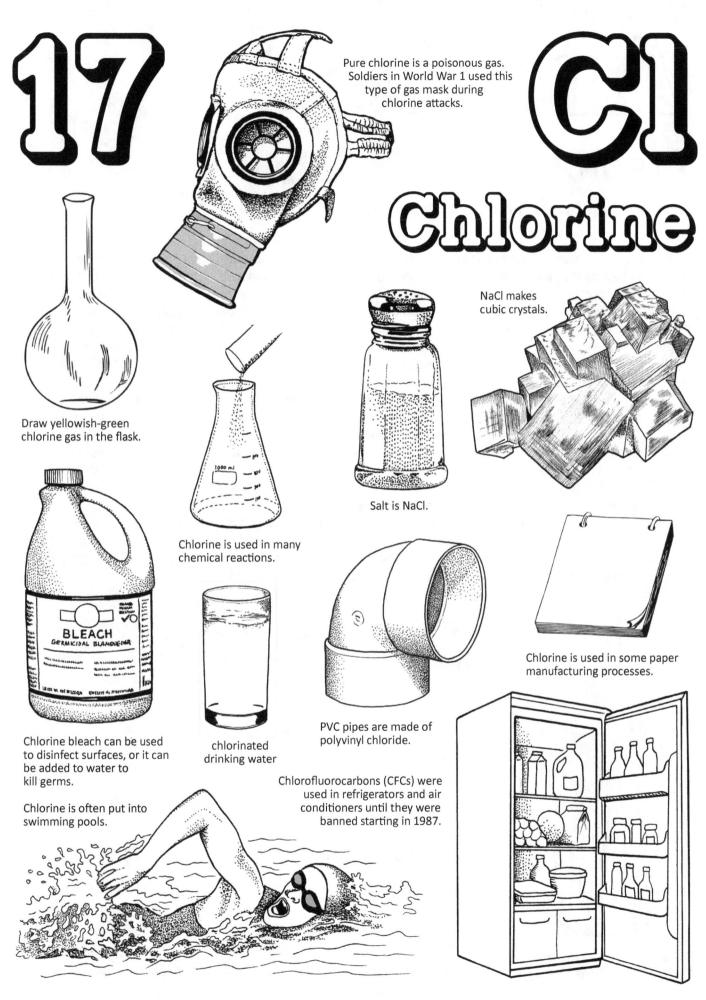

17

Pure chlorine is a poisonous gas. Soldiers in World War 1 used this type of gas mask during chlorine attacks.

Cl
Chlorine

Draw yellowish-green chlorine gas in the flask.

Chlorine is used in many chemical reactions.

Salt is NaCl.

NaCl makes cubic crystals.

Chlorine is used in some paper manufacturing processes.

Chlorine bleach can be used to disinfect surfaces, or it can be added to water to kill germs.

chlorinated drinking water

PVC pipes are made of polyvinyl chloride.

Chlorine is often put into swimming pools.

Chlorofluorocarbons (CFCs) were used in refrigerators and air conditioners until they were banned starting in 1987.

BLEACH
GERMICIDAL BLANQUEDOR

Ar 18

18 protons
22 neutrons
18 electrons

Atomic mass: 39.9

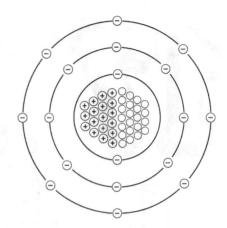

Argon

From the Greek word "argos" meaning "lazy"

Argon is a harmless gas that is found in the air all around us. It makes up almost 1% of our atmosphere, and is twice as abundant as water vapor. It was discovered in 1894 by Sir William Ramsay and Lord Rayleigh. They used a technique suggested by Henry Cavendish, who had investigated gases back in the late 1700s. They exposed normal air to both electricity and a very alkaline substance until all the oxygen, nitrogen, and carbon dioxide were gone. They found that there was still a gas left in the jar. When they tested this gas they found that it would not react with any other element, so they called it "argon," meaning "lazy." Today, argon is produced by simply chilling air until all the gases turn to liquid, then letting the temperature rise slowly and catching each element as it "boils" off and becomes a gas again.

Argon isn't the only lazy gas. It belongs to the family of elements called the noble gases, found in the column all the way to the right on the Periodic Table. These gases don't react with other elements because their outer electron shell is completely full. They don't need to gain or lose any electrons.

Since argon is so nonreactive, it is ideal for use in places where safety around heat is a concern, such as in graphite electric furnaces (used for manufacturing of steel) and in gas metal arc welding. Argon acts like a shield around the intense heat of the weld. It is also perfect for filling all types of light bulbs, both incandescent and fluorescent.

When argon is used in lasers, they emit a blue-green light. These lasers are used in specialized microscopy, in surgery, in some DNA sequencers, for inspecting semiconductor wafers, and in laser light shows.

A lesser-known use for argon is in the poultry industry where it is used to butcher large numbers of chickens very quickly. Argon gas is heavier than air, so it will hover at ground level. Once the birds begin breathing the argon, they fall asleep before being asphyxiated, so they never experience any pain or fear.

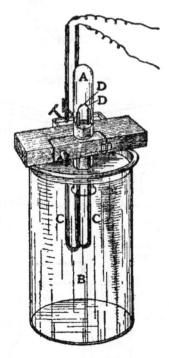

The apparatus that Ramsay and Rayleigh used to isolate argon.

Sir William Ramsay

Lord Rayleigh (John Strutt)

Normally, argon floats around as single atoms.

HArF Argon fluorohydride

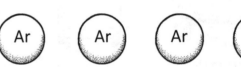

In the year 2000, some Finnish scientists cooled argon down to -265° C, and mixed it with hydrogen fluoride while exposing it to ultraviolet radiation. HArF molecules formed, but they quickly fell apart when the temperature began rising.

18 Argon Ar

Argon is used for humane slaughtering of poultry.

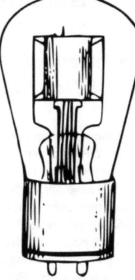

Argon is used to fill all kinds of light bulbs.

Argon lasers are used for eye surgery. They make a bright blue line of light.

This is a cutaway view of a graphite furnace, used to melt steel. Electricity flows through the graphite rods and produces a bowl of hot, liquid metal.

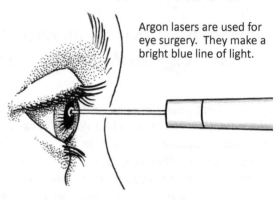

Replacing regular air with argon will keep paint and varnish from drying and oxidizing.

OXYGEN BLOCKER

Glove boxes can be filled with an inert gas like argon so that technicians can work with materials that can't be exposed to oxygen or nitrogen.

Gas metal arc welding uses argon to shield the hot welding area from the oxygen in the air.

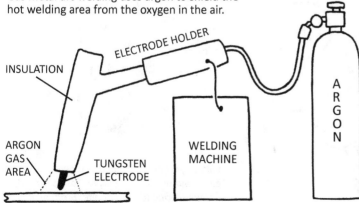

INSULATION

ELECTRODE HOLDER

ARGON GAS AREA

TUNGSTEN ELECTRODE

WELDING MACHINE

ARGON

K

Potassium

19
protons
20 neutrons
19 electrons

Atomic mass: 39.1

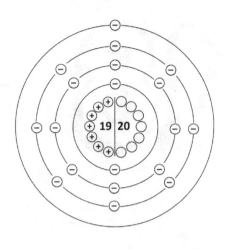

From the word "potash" (ashes from plant leaves)
The letter K is from the Arabic word for potash, "kali" (al-kali)

Pure potassium had never been seen before Sir Humphry Davy produced it in 1807 using electricity to draw the potassium atoms out of a solution of caustic potash (KOH). A few months after this he would use the same technique to isolate pure sodium. Neither of these elements ever occur in their pure state in nature because they are so reactive. Their reactivity is due to the fact that they have one lonely electron in their outer shell, and they are desperate to give it away. Both potassium and sodium in their pure state are soft, shiny silver metals.

In the earth's crust, potassium is found primarily in rocks called feldspar, especially orthoclase feldspar. It also occurs naturally in deposits of saltpeter, KNO_3, and KCl, potassium chloride. Hundreds of years ago, saltpeter was found to be one of the key ingredients needed to make gunpowder, along with sulfur and charcoal.

Potassium is an essential mineral to both animals and plants. (Potash, the source of potassium before the 20th century, was made from the ashes of plants.) In our own bodies, potassium and sodium flow in and out of cells through channels called sodium-potassium pumps.   These pumps are especially important in nerve cells, which use them to transmit electrical impulses. Foods high in potassium include potatoes, spinach, avocados, and bananas.

Potassium plays a role in many chemical reactions, both as a reactant and as an end product. Potassium compounds are used in the manufacturing of inks, dyes, stains, soaps, bleach, matches, glass, and tanned leather.

Potassium compounds are used in food preparation. Potassium bisulfate, $KHSO_3$, is a preservative and potassium bromate, $KBrO_3$, is used to strengthen bread dough. Potassium chloride, KCl, is used as a salt (NaCl) substitute.

Potassium chloride, KCl, is a very useful potassium compound. It is used for de-icing sidewalks, as flux in glass manufacturing, as a fertilizer, as a source of radiation in scientific research, in petroleum and natural gas extraction, in heat packs that provide instant heat, and in home water softeners.

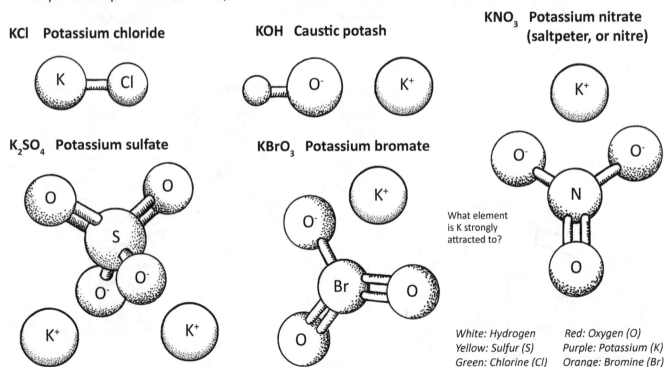

KCl Potassium chloride

KOH Caustic potash

**KNO_3 Potassium nitrate
(saltpeter, or nitre)**

K_2SO_4 Potassium sulfate

$KBrO_3$ Potassium bromate

What element is K strongly attracted to?

White: Hydrogen   Red: Oxygen (O)
Yellow: Sulfur (S)   Purple: Potassium (K)
Green: Chlorine (Cl)   Orange: Bromine (Br)

19

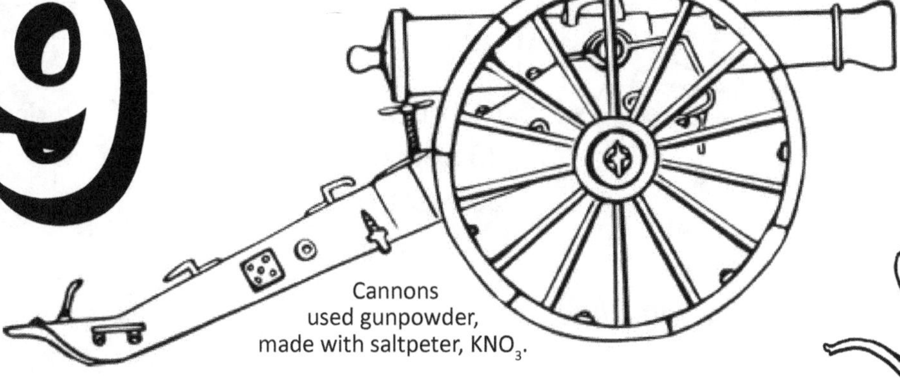

Cannons used gunpowder, made with saltpeter, KNO_3.

K

Potassium

These foods are high in potassium...

bananas

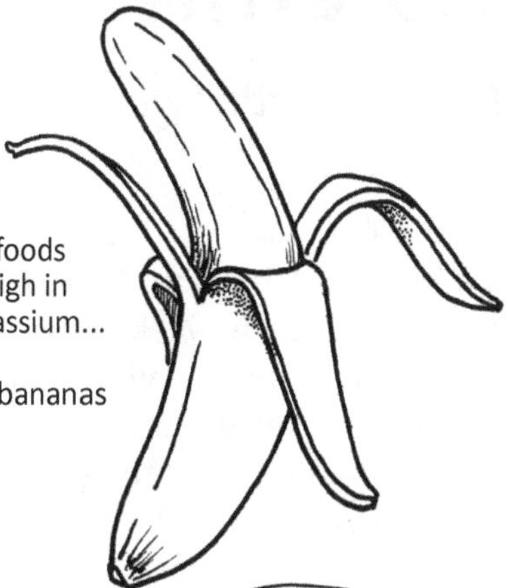

Plants need potassium as one of their essential minerals.

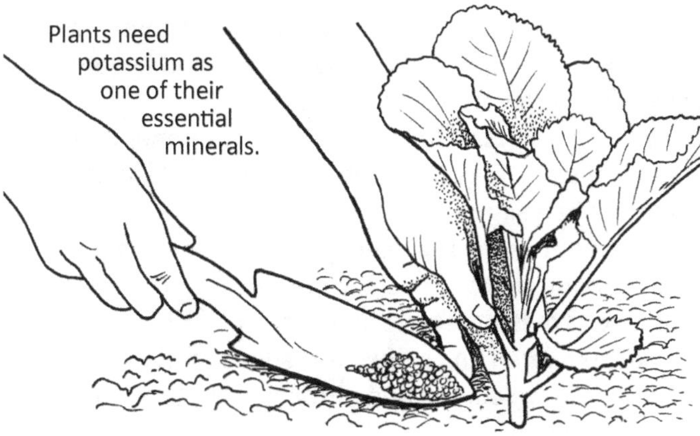

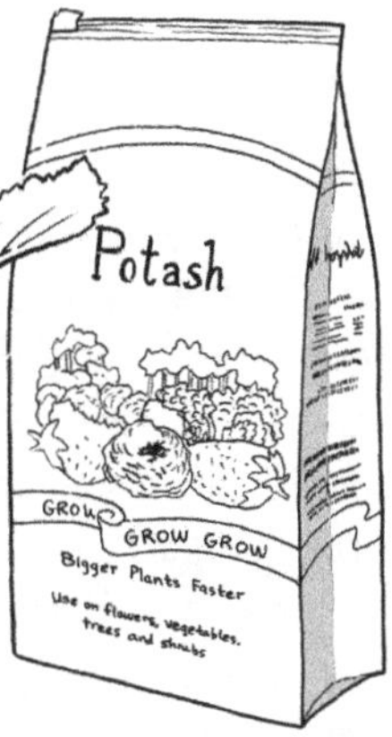

Potash

GROW GROW GROW
Bigger Plants Faster
Use on flowers, vegetables, trees and shrubs

sweet potatoes

avocados

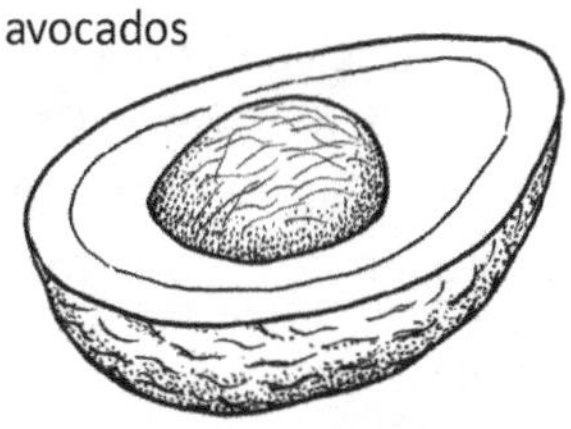

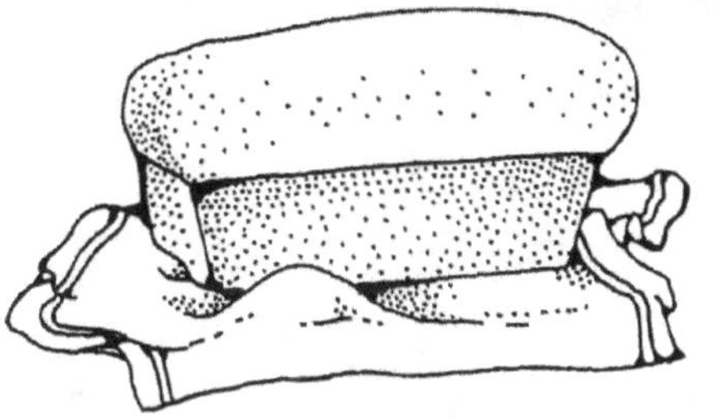

$KBrO_3$ is used in commercial bread baking.

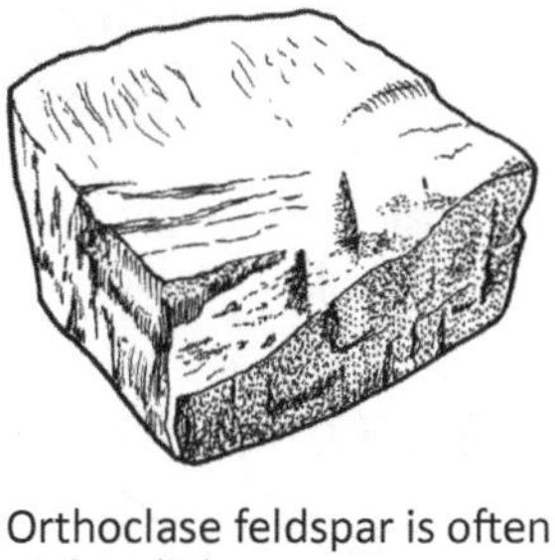

Orthoclase feldspar is often pink or light orange.

LIQUID SOAP Citrus

10 FL OZ
295 ml Great Brand

The sodium-potassium pump is found in cell membranes.

Na^+

K^+

The membrane is made of molecules called phospholipids.

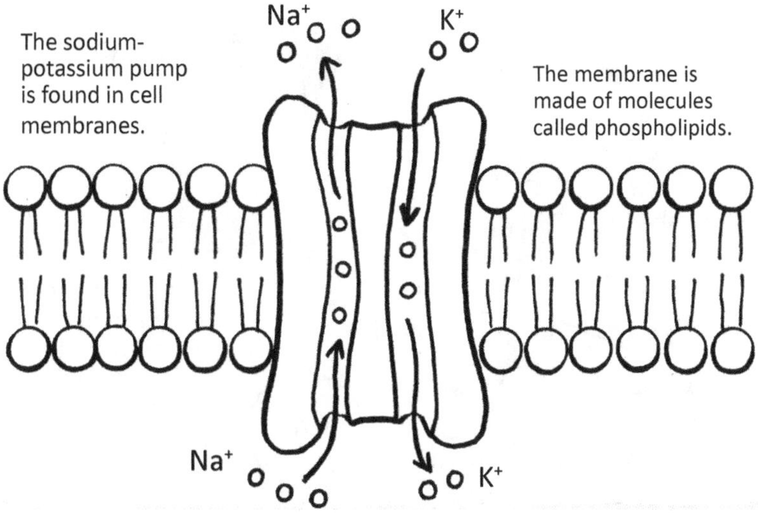

Na^+

K^+

Potassium is used in soap making.

Potassium bicarbonate is in some carbonated beverages.

Ca

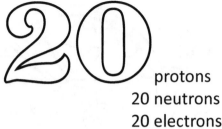

protons
20 neutrons
20 electrons

Atomic mass: 40.08

Calcium

From the Greek word "calx," meaning "lime"

Calcium is yet another element discovered by Sir Humphry Davy. Its existence was already suspected, but it was not isolated until 1808, when Davy used electrolysis to pull pure calcium out of a chemical solution. Within the space of a few weeks, Davy had also discovered the elements above and below calcium on the Periodic Table: magnesium, barium and strontium. Most people expect pure calcium to be white, like so many of the calcium compounds they know, but pure calcium is a soft, gray metal.

In the crust of the earth, calcium is found in these minerals: limestone, chalk, aragonite (all of these are $CaCO_3$), gypsum ($CaSO_4$), fluorite (CaF_2), and apatite ($Ca_{10}(PO_4)_6(OH)_2$). When limestone is squeezed and heated it turns into marble, a metamorphic rock that has been widely used for buildings and statues.

Calcium plays many vital roles in the body. Besides being an important building material for bones and teeth, calcium is used in the transmission of signals in the nervous system, in contraction of muscle cells, as cofactors for many enzymes, in protein synthesis, and in the fertilization of an egg cell.

Many mollusks (clams, snails, oysters, etc.) can take calcium out of the sea water and use it to build shells. Natural chalk deposits, such as the White Cliffs of Dover, are made of the shells of microscopic single-celled protozoa called foraminiferans and coccolithophores. England and Denmark have the greatest number of chalk cliffs.

Pure calcium metal is used in steel making, where it binds to oxygen and sulfur. It is added to aluminum alloys to give the metal greater strength. It is used as a "getter" to remove oxygen and nitrogen from tubes of inert gas (such as argon). Calcium hydride, CaH_2 is used as a source of hydrogen.

Calcium compounds are found in many household products such as baking ingredients, drain cleaner, toothpaste, antacids, and medicines. It can also be found in maintenance-free car batteries.

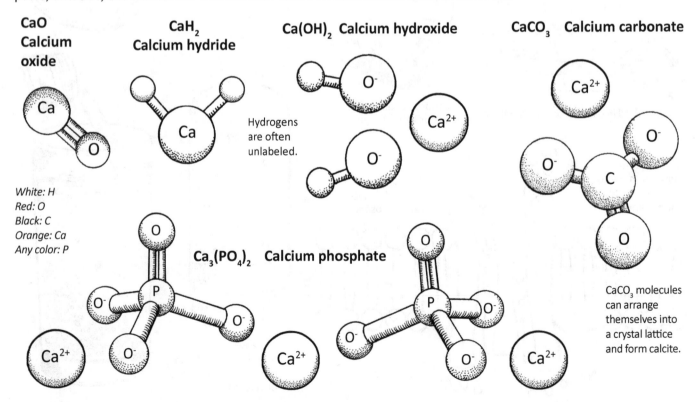

CaO
Calcium oxide

CaH₂
Calcium hydride

Ca(OH)₂ Calcium hydroxide

Hydrogens are often unlabeled.

CaCO₃ Calcium carbonate

White: H
Red: O
Black: C
Orange: Ca
Any color: P

Ca₃(PO₄)₂ Calcium phosphate

CaCO₃ molecules can arrange themselves into a crystal lattice and form calcite.

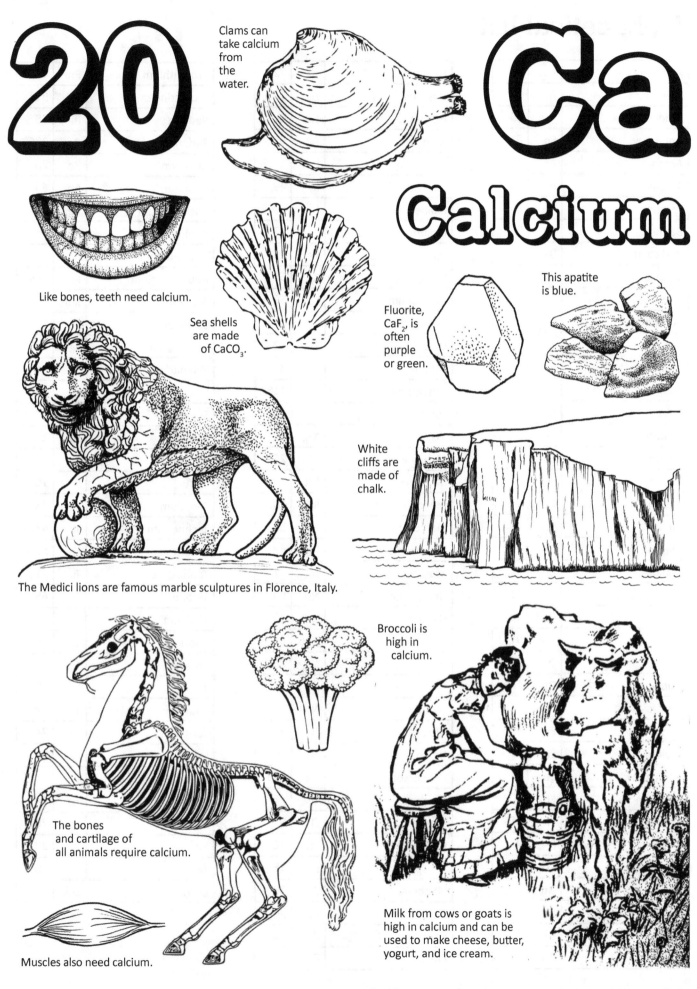

20

Clams can take calcium from the water.

Ca

Calcium

Like bones, teeth need calcium.

Sea shells are made of $CaCO_3$.

Fluorite, CaF_2, is often purple or green.

This apatite is blue.

White cliffs are made of chalk.

The Medici lions are famous marble sculptures in Florence, Italy.

Broccoli is high in calcium.

The bones and cartilage of all animals require calcium.

Muscles also need calcium.

Milk from cows or goats is high in calcium and can be used to make cheese, butter, yogurt, and ice cream.

Alphabetical list

Actinium	Ac	89		Hafnium	Hf	72		Promethium	Pm	61
Aluminum	Al	13		Hassium	Hs	108		Protactinium	Pa	91
Americium	Am	95		Helium	He	2		Radium	Ra	88
Antimony	Sb	51		Holmium	Ho	67		Radon	Rn	386
Argon	Ar	18		Hydrogen	H	1		Rhenium	Re	75
Arsenic	As	33		Indium	In	49		Rhodium	Rh	45
Astatine	At	85		Iodine	I	53		Roentgenium	Rg	111
Barium	Ba	56		Iridium	Ir	77		Rubidium	Rb	37
Berkelium	Bk	97		Iron	Fe	26		Ruthenium	Ru	44
Beryllium	Be	4		Krypton	Kr	36		Rutherfordium	Rf	104
Bismuth	Bi	83		Lanthanum	La	57		Samarium	Sm	62
Bohrium	Bh	107		Lawrencium	Lr	103		Scandium	Sc	21
Boron	B	5		Lead	Pb	82		Seaborgium	Sg	106
Bromine	Br	35		Lithium	Li	3		Selenium	Se	34
Cadmium	Cd	49		Livermorium	Lv	116		Silicon	Si	14
Calcium	Ca	20		Lutetium	Lu	71		Silver	Ag	47
Californium	Cf	98		Magnesium	Mg	12		Sodium	Na	11
Carbon	C	6		Manganese	Mn	25		Strontium	Sr	38
Cerium	Ce	58		Meitnerium	Mt	109		Sulfur	S	16
Cesium	Cs	55		Mendelevium	Md	101		Tantalum	Ta	73
Chlorine	Cl	17		Mercury	Hg	80		Technetium	Tc	43
Chromium	Cr	24		Molybdenum	Mo	42		Tellurium	Te	52
Cobalt	Co	27		Moscovium	Mc	115		Tennessine	Ts	117
Copernicium	Cn	112		Neodymium	Nd	60		Terbium	Tb	65
Copper	Cu	25		Neon	Ne	10		Thallium	Tl	81
Curium	Cm	96		Neptunium	Np	93		Thorium	Th	90
Darmstadtium	Ds	110		Nickel	Ni	28		Thulium	Tm	69
Dubnium	Db	105		Nihonium	Nh	113		Tin	Sn	50
Dysprosium	Dy	66		Niobium	Nb	41		Titanium	Ti	22
Einsteinium	Es	99		Nitrogen	N	7		Tungsten	W	74
Erbium	Er	68		Nobelium	No	102		Uranium	U	92
Europium	Eu	63		Oganesson	Og	118		Vanadium	V	23
Fermium	Fm	100		Osmium	Os	76		Xenon	Xe	54
Flerovium	Fl	114		Oxygen	O	8		Ytterbium	Yb	70
Fluorine	F	9		Palladium	Pd	46		Yttrium	Y	39
Francium	Fr	87		Phosphorus	P	15		Zinc	Zn	30
Gadolinium	Gd	64		Platinum	Pt	78		Zirconium	Zr	40
Gallium	Ga	31		Plutonium	Pu	94				
Germanium	Ge	32		Potassium	K	19				
Gold	Au	79		Praseodymium	Pr	59				

© *The Chemical Elements Coloring and Activity Book* by Ellen Johnston McHenry

CPSIA information can be obtained
at www.ICGtesting.com
Printed in the USA
BVHW020423070723
666783BV00012B/1120